Dual Mode Cellular

Lawrence Harte

P.T. Steiner Publishing Co.

Published by P.T. Steiner Publishing Co.
200 Bursca Drive, Suite 100
Bridgeville, Pennsylvania 15017 U.S.A.

First American Edition — January 1992.

Photos by the author unless otherwise indicated.

ISBN 0-9631965-0-2

Library of Congress Catalog Card Number 91-68135.

Printed in the United States of America.

ACKNOWLEDGEMENT

I want to thank all the people who gave technical and emotional support for the creation of this book. In many cases, published sources were not available on this subject area. Many people from manufacturers, service providers, and trade associations gave their personal, precious time and for this, I sincerely thank and respect them.

Of the numerous manufacturers' representatives who have dedicated their time to creating the standards that will make Digital Cellular a reality, I must thank the folowing representatives: Philip Christopher, Paul Wilkinson and Jerry Smeltzer from Audiovox; Robert Spoer from Teknekron Communications Systems; Hisatomi-San, Matsuoka-San and Yamamoto-San from Toshiba; Steve Jones from NEC; Richard Levine from Beta Laboratories; Dave Whipple and Larry Nutting from Hewlett Packard; Ron Bohaychuk and Krister Raith from Ericsson; George Peponides from PCSI; Prem Sood from Sharp; Al Sacuta from IMM; Bob Dixon from OmniPoint Data; Eli Strich from Qualcomm; Reed Fisher from Oki; Dave Sattler, Mike McLaughlin, Bob Picha, and Tom Auchter from Motorola; Peter George and Greg Aurelius from Marconi; Simon O'Neill and Eric Tomlin from Technophone; Simon Mizikovsky from Sony; Howard Lester from GE; David DeVaney and Imamura-San from Astronet; Peter Nurse and Mike Parr from Hughes Network Systems; Mike Bonnin and Saiful Hug from LCC; and Phil Treventi, John Marinho, and James Yu from AT&T.

Thanks to service provider representatives such as Dr. Tae Won Oh from NYNEX; Tom Richter from BellSouth; Terry Watts from South Western Bell; Limond Grindstaff from PacTel; Frank Wurtz and Mike Haberman from Bell Atlantic; and David Danaeé from McCaw.

Thanks also to trade association representatives, Gary Brunt representing CTIA; Eric Schimmel from TIA; and Fred Link from Radio Club of America.

Specific mention must go to my family and Jacquelyn Gottlieb who gave me emotional support throughout its development. There are so many other people, too numerous to mention, who have taken their time to answer questions and provide information. Many have taken a personal commitment to the development of quality communications systems. My sincere hope is this book will be a starting and reference point for many new engineers entering this field.

TABLE OF CONTENTS

Chapter 3 Analog Cellular System Network

Chapter 7 Cellular System Economics

Chapter 8 World Cellular Technologies

Dual Mode Cellular

Cellular systems worldwide are experiencing rapid growth rates. The concept of cellular has allowed a gradual capacity expansion as the number of subscribers in a given area increases. The cost of this expansion and demand for more sophisticated features has led to the development of digital cellular technology. The focus of this book is to describe Dual Mode cellular technology for managers and engineers. It explains key functions, design considerations, and a systems perspective to the technology.

This book is divided into three major sections. First is analog cellular description which provides a functional and technical overview of existing cellular equipment. Second is the description of the new dual mode cellular technology with reference to the evolution from analog cellular. Finally, considerations such as costs, patents, implementation options, and alternate technologies are discussed.

The introduction describes the need for Dual Mode Cellular. The development of the U.S. dual mode standard (IS-54) was accelerated by the cellular service providers. While the analog cellular system was supposed to have essentially unlimited expansibility, unforeseen aspects caused significant expansion problems. To produce a more cost effective technology, the cellular service providers worked with the TIA (Telecommunications Industry Association) to produce a new cellular standard.

ANALOG CELLULAR

Chapter 1 provides a general overview of the operation of Analog Equipment. For the experienced cellular engineer, this will be a very basic description. I recommend this section to everyone who may have some questions about Analog cellular operation. Chapter 2 is a technical description of analog cellular mobile stations. It includes RF channel structure, Signaling, and Call Processing. This is a good technical review and gives reasons why functions were developed. Chapter 3 is a technical description of the analog cellular network and network system planning considerations.

DUAL MODE CELLULAR

Chapter 4 describes the operation of dual mode equipment with reference to the existing analog system. The TDMA (Time Division Multiple Access) structure, signaling, and new capabilities are presented. Chapter 5 gives a technical description for dual mode terminal equipments. Included are modulation techniques, channel structure, equalization, speech coding, signaling, call processing, power amplifier characteristics, and error detection and correction. Chapter 6 gives a technical description for the dual mode cellular network. Included are equipment requirements and implementation methods.

DESIGN CONSIDERATIONS

Chapter 7 provides ideas for cellular system economics which describes the dual mode conversion process. Specifically, what will mobiles cost the consumers, carriers and equipment replacement program options. Chapter 8 describes alternate cellular technologies. Commercially available FDMA, TDMA, and CDMA technologies are discussed.

This industry contains acronyms and terms which can create misunderstandings of cellular technology. Appendix I provides for definitions. Appendix II defines acronyms. Appendix III lists applicable standards. Appendix IV is a matrix of World Cellular Systems.

Digital Cellular is a new technology. Though the industry standards for which this book is based have been accepted, they are subject to change. It is not anticipated that significant changes will occur, however, EIA standards are paramount when compared with information in this book.

For the past few years I have been making presentations and conducting training on digital cellular technology. I have included illustrations and reference materials that have been helpful in those presentations to further clarify the text.

Introduction

I.1 BRIEF HISTORY OF MOBILE RADIO

While Mobile Radio has been in use for approximately 70 years and the cellular concept was conceived in the 1940s, public cellular mobile radio was not introduced in the U.S. until 1983. Today's electronics technology was needed to allow the introduction of the cellular system we know today. Significant developments in mobile radio technology include broadcast radio, simplex (two way, one speaker at a time) and duplex (two way, simultaneous) transmission, PSTN connection, trunking connection ability, and spectral efficiency.

In the beginning of the twentieth century, mobile radio effectiveness was limited to shipboard use due to the high power requirements and bulky tube radio technology. Automotive systems in the 1920s operated on 6 volt batteries with a limited storage capacity. In addition, mechanical design of the tubes was susceptible to vibration resulting in poor performance and reliability[1].

One of the first useful means of automotive mobile radio occurred in 1928 by the Detroit police department [2]. Transmission was broadcast from a central location and only could be received by the mobile radios.

With the beginning of economic depression, equipment power consumption requirements, and the need for vacuum tubes that could withstand vibration, the introduction of the first two way mobile application was delayed until 1933. This simplex AM (Amplitude Modulation) push to talk system was introduced by the police department in Bayonne, New Jersey. The first FM (Frequency Modulation) mobile transmission (two frequency simplex) occurred in the Connecticut State Police at Hartford in 1940 [3].

The first step towards mobile radio connection with the land line telephone network was established in St. Louis in 1946. It was called an "urban" system and only supported three channels [4].

Full duplex (two way simultaneous) mobile transmission did not occur until the mid-1950s when RCA completed a controversial contract for the City of Philadelphia police department. While the specifications were beyond the technical capability at that time, a limited form of mobile FM duplex was developed [5].

Early radio systems required dedicated channels for a small group of users which limited the efficiency of the radio spectrum. Trunking allows the automatic sharing of several communications channels between a large group of users. In 1964, the IMTS (Improved Mobile Telephone Service) MJ system was introduced. This was the first real step towards mobile telephony as we know it today. It supported automatic channel selection, trunking, and allowed full duplex transmission [6].

The lack of available frequency bands restricted the total number of radios that could be supported on one system. Early mobile applications required much larger bandwidths than today due to the lack of crystal controlled stability. Wide bandwidth requirements, up to 20 times as much[1], were required to allow for the frequency drift [7]. The early opinion of the FCC was to serve the majority of users resulting in much of the available commercial spectrum being assigned to broadcast systems [8]. While trunking and more stable transmitters increased the efficiency of spectrum utilization, a majority of the population could not be served with the early spectrum allocation. In 1976, people were placed on waiting lists to get a mobile phone [9].

Mobile radio had been in demand for many years but its high cost kept its market share small until the early 1980s. Market studies had shown a large demand at low prices [10]. This demand has been met by the low costs of cellular technology.

I.2 CELLULAR MOBILE RADIO SYSTEM

While the cellular concept originated at Bell Laboratories in 1947 [11], and the first automatic cellular commercial system started operation in October 1983 in Chicago, one of the first cellular systems started in Detroit in 1949. A taxicab dispatch system required the use of small coverage areas (cell sites) to provide service to hundreds of square miles. While frequencies were re-used in alternate cells, switching between channels was manually accomplished by the users at predetermined locations [12].

The basic goals for a cellular system according to the *Bell System Technical Journal* are:

(1) Large subscriber capacity; (2) Efficient use of spectrum; (3) Nationwide compatibility; (4) Widespread availability; (5) Adaptability to traffic density; (6) Service to vehicles and portables; (7) Support of special services; (8) Telephone quality of service; and (9) Affordability.

---

1   Original AM broadcasts required 100 kHz of bandwidth as compared with the Single Sideband AirPhone (trademark of GTE) system which allows only 5kHz of bandwidth per channel.

The cellular concept allows small radio coverage areas to become part of a larger system by interconnecting via a central switching office. This allows a call to be maintained when the mobile station moves from one coverage area to another by switching the radio channel to the next cell site location. All transmission is basically somewhat cellular in nature anyway. When distance from a transmitter increases, it is possible to reuse frequencies. A cellular system allows the determination of boundaries of cells by setting transmitter power levels of the base stations. By lowering the transmitter power, the effective range (coverage area) is reduced so radio channels can be reused repeatedly at different coverage areas. While adjoining cell site areas cannot use the same radio frequencies, each cell site area can support several radio channels.

Cellular system expansion is possible with the addition of radio towers which have smaller cell site coverage areas. Since each cell site can offer several radio channels, the more cell sites in a given area, the more available radio channels.

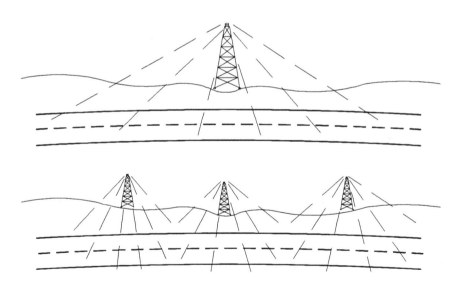

Figure I.1 Cellular System Expansion by Cell Site Splitting

As the cellular system grows, towers are added which result in immense expansibility. In theory this is true; in practice, unforeseen factors have caused significant expansion problems. Obtaining cell site land rights and construction costs are high [13], hampering expansion.

To maintain a call while moving throughout several cell site areas, a call may be transferred between adjacent cell sites while the call is in progress. The limited technology available in 1947, and lack of available frequency allocation, prohibited its implementation until March 1977 when the FCC authorized a test system in Chicago. Computers and switching systems were not developed to handle the large amount and fast switching required in a cellular system until the 1970s.

I.3 ANALOG CELLULAR

When the current U.S. cellular system was introduced in 1983, it was termed AMPS (Advanced Mobile Phone Service) which is now defined by EIA (Electronics Industries Association) specification EIA-553, Base Station to Mobile Station Compatibility Standard. Mobile and Base Station units that are manufactured to this specification should be capable of working the U.S. system.

In Figure I.2, we see that only one mobile phone can communicate on a channel for the Analog system. Today's system requires additional cell sites to increase the total number of available channels. Each cell site costs approximately $500,000 to $1,000,000 for start-up costs [14]. With more cell sites there will be telephone lines between towers. Leased from the phone company, these lines are expensive and increase operating costs. With an analog system, as the number of subscribers increases, the average cost per subscriber increases.

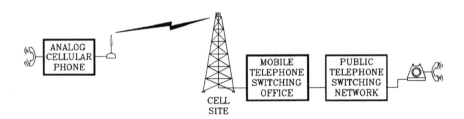

Figure I.2 Analog Cellular System

I.3.1. Innovations

The ability to communicate reliably almost anywhere in this country is a substantial achievement. Products have changed since their introduction in 1983 predominantly in size and capability.

I.3.1.1. Pocket Telephones

In 1976, the first prototype Mobile Station weighed over 80 pounds [15]. Today, this entire unit may be packaged together into a portable unit that can be stored in a pocket. One of the first and smallest cellular phones to become available was the Micro-Tac. Shown below, its size is 13.5 cubic inches and its weight is only 10.7 oz. with battery. The trend today is toward the use of portables as shown in Las Vegas where over 80% of the subscribers are using portables [16].

Figure I.3 Micro-Tac pocket telephone (courtesy of Motorola)

I.3.1.2. Multiple Use Telephones

Units can be classified in three categories: portables, mobiles, and transportables. Portable telephones are limited in maximum output power to .6 Watts for safety reasons. Mobile phones are allowed to emit over

Figure I.4 Audiovox CTX 5000 Portable (courtesy of Audiovox)

3 Watts which may be necessary to ensure quality transmission in large cellular areas. A transportable may transmit a full three watts and also be portable.

Some portable units now connect to a booster which increases the power capability. As a portable, it is only capable of .6 Watt transmission, but when attached to the booster, then it becomes capable of transmitting a full 3 watts.

I.3.1.3. Fixed Subscriber

In disaster situations, communications for public service and safety related companies is essential. In cases of floods, hurricanes, and earthquakes, land line phone service has become unavailable for many weeks or more. A backup cellular phone can generate its own dial tone and operates as a standard telephone line. The operator cannot tell the difference between the cellular phone and the land line operation.

Figure I.5 Fixed Subscriber Backup System (courtesy of Telular)

I.3.1.4. Nationwide Networking

When the cellular systems first began operation, they were allocated by MSA (Metropolitan Statistical Area) and RSA (Rural Service Areas) areas. Mobiles operating in their designated home MSA or RSA had full capability. When operating in one of the 743 other systems, only a more limited operation was possible. Authorization to originate calls may not be automatic and calls did not automatically reach the mobile when out of the system. It is the goal of the FCC to create a seamless system where the use of the cellular system is transparent to the user no matter which system the subscriber operates [17]. This can now be accomplished by standard system of interconnects that enables authorized access to be immediate and calls to be routed automatically to the system that is being visited [18].

I.4. DUAL MODE DIGITAL CELLULAR

If the cellular system works well today, why do we need a new system? In the United States, no guarantee exists that a cellular system operator will be allowed to build a tower where needed. In addition, minimum cell sizes, cell site fixed and operational costs have resulted in expansion challenges.

For the past two years, manufacturers and service providers have been developing a new technology termed Digital Cellular. It was created to allow cellular expansion at reasonable cost. The development of the U.S. Dual Mode standard (IS-54) was accelerated by the cellular system operators to help meet the demand of the increasing number of subscribers. In 1988, the CTIA (Cellular Telecommunications Industry Association) commissioned the ARTS (Advanced Radio Technology Subcommittee) to review alternate technologies to allow for cost effective cellular expansion [19]. This resulted in the creation of the UPR (User Performance Requirements) which defined the necessary technology for the next generation of cellular technology, "Dual Mode Cellular."

To allow for a gradual transition, a Dual Mode cellular transceiver consists of both Analog (FM) and digital transmission sections. When digital service is available, it will automatically attempt access to obtain digital channels. If a digital channel is not available, it will attempt access for an analog channel.

The digital system accepted by the CTIA allows users to share a radio channel by time division. Each user is assigned to specific time slots for transmission and reception. This system has been termed TDMA (Time Division Multiple Access).

Figure I-6 displays the basic operation of the Digital Cellular transmit section. Audio signals are converted into digital pulses by an Analog to Digital Converter. The digital signals are then characterized and compressed in the Speech CoDec section. This resultant digital signal is then converted to a radio signal for transmission. The radio signal is transmitted in bursts to allow time sharing with other users.

The receiver section for Digital cellular works in reverse. It receives on its assigned time slot, expands the compressed voice information, and converts it back to an Analog signal.

The first generation allows three users to share the same channel. With this triple capacity, less cell sites are needed resulting in less interconnecting of leased phone lines. Initially with this Digital system, as the number of subscribers increases, the average cost per subscriber will decrease.

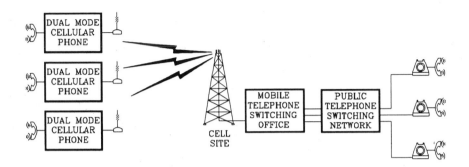

Figure I.6 Dual Mode Cellular System

I.5. DIGITAL ONLY CELLULAR

Dual Mode phones consist of two transceiver assemblies in one box which is not cost effective. In addition, accessing the system is accomplished via the outdated control channels which can be optimized to support more users and additional features. A third type of Cellular Service to be available in a few years will be Digital Only cellular. Digital Only uses a completely different type of control channel which will not be available until around 1993. While these phones can be smaller and lighter, they will not work in an Analog system. Because it will be many years before Digital Only service becomes available everywhere, Dual Mode phones will be in use for many years.

I.6. WORLD COMPATIBILITY

In 1990, the United States had the largest cellular system in the world. Since its official introduction in 1983, many countries have adopted the U.S. cellular standard which allows the same units to operate in many countries. As a general rule, Europe is very diversified and has many types of cellular systems which are not compatible. North and South America are U.S. cellular compatible. Table I.1 is a list of countries which are (or will be) compatible with the U.S. cellular system.

Many of the compatible systems in other countries may adopt the U.S. digital standard. Because of the high cost of the digital equipment and limited problems with cellular expansion, some countries will not need to convert to digital capability for many years.

Table I.1 Systems Compatible With U.S.

Country	Start Date	No. of Subscribers
Antigua & Barbuda	19XX	-
Argentina	1989	3,200
Australia	1986	210,000
Barbados	1990	-
Bahamas	19XX	-
Bermuda	19XX	-
Bolivia	1990	-
Brazil	1990	30,000
British Virgin Islands	19XX	-
Brunei	1989	5,000
Canada	1985	540,000
Cayman Islands	1987	-
Chile	1989	6,800
Columbia	1991	-
Costa Rica	1989	700
Curacao	19XX	-
Czechoslovakia	19XX	-
Dominican Republic	1987	1,200
Egypt	19XX	-
Gabon	1991	-
Grenada	19XX	-
Guadeloupe	19XX	-
Guam	19XX	-
Guatemala	19XX	-
Hong Kong	1985	34,200
Indonesia	19XX	-
Israel	1986	10,500
Jamaica	19XX	-
Jordan	19XX	-
Kenya	19XX	-
Malaysia	19XX	-
Mexico	1989	34,000
Netherlands Antilles	19XX	-
New Zealand	1987	42,000
Panama	19XX	-
Peru	19XX	-
Philippines	1989	8,000
Puerto Rico	19XX	-

Table I.1 Systems Compatible With U.S. (continued)

Country	Start Date	No. of Subscribers
Singapore	1988	28,000
Samoa (American)	1987	300
South Korea	1984	66,400
St. Kitts	1989	-
St. Lucia	19XX	-
St. Maarten	19XX	-
St. Vincent & Grenadines	19XX	-
Taiwan	1989	57,500
Thailand	19XX	-
Uruguay	19XX	-
U.S.A.	1983	6,300,000
Venezuela	1988	8,000
Virgin Islands	19XX	-
Zaire	19XX	-

Note: Some starting dates and numbers of subscribers were not available at press time.

(Source: FinTech - Mobile Communications, Issue 68, Financial Times Newsletters, Tower House, November 22, 1990; U.S. Dept of Commerce, System Listings, 1990)

I.7. UPGRADING TO DIGITAL CELLULAR

Why a customer will upgrade to Digital Cellular service is a major issue. Higher voice quality, reduced blockage, and less dropped calls are some reasons why a subscriber may convert. However, the bottom line is, Digital Cellular is more cost effective.

For the conversion to a Digital system, existing cell sites can be modified at minimal cost to allow more users on the system. While Digital Cellular service may not be activated until early 1992, mobiles will be available prior to service availability. Dual Mode service will appear in congested cities first, such as Los Angeles, Chicago, and New York with Digital service conversion for the entire country in approximately five years. Actual conversion for the existing subscriber may be as simple as replacement of the transceiver. Others may require the installation of an entire new system. Due to the added complexity, Dual Mode handhelds may not enter the market until 1992 or 1993 [20].

I.8. SUMMARY

Since 1983, the Analog Cellular system has served over 5 million subscribers. To allow cost effective system expansion, digital cellular technology has been developed. The first digital phones will be Dual Mode capable, allowing operation on both Analog and Digital channels. While Analog phones will continue to work in the new system, digital capable phones will be higher in quality and eventually less expensive to use.

As Digital service becomes more available, the price of the Digital phones will be reduced. Also, the advanced technology which will be utilized will make the units smaller and more compact in several years. However, for now, the Dual Mode phones have entered the market and will offer the best of both analog and digital features.

While the growth of the cellular system in the U.S. has been extensive, the growth outside has been great. Over 52 countries provide cellular service conforming to the U.S. AMPS system.

Converting subscribers to digital service may be a challenge. But, its cost-effectiveness, higher voice quality, reduced blockage, and less dropped calls should prove to be convincing advantages.

References:

[1] Link, Fred, former president and owner of Link Radio. Interview, February 17, 1991.

[2] George Calhoun, *Digital Cellular*, (Artech House, 1988), p. 26.

[3] Edward Singer, *Land Mobile Radio Systems*, (Prentice Hall, New Jersey, 1989), p. 10.

[4] American Telephone and Telegraph Company, *The Bell System Technical Journal*, (Murray Hill, New Jersey), January 1979, Vol. 58, No. 1, p. 3.

[5] Link interview.

[6] *The Bell System Technical Journal*, Jan. 1979, p. 3.

[7] Link interview.

[8] Calhoun, pp. 45-46

[9] William Lee, *Cellular Communications* , (McGraw Hill 1989), p. 2.

[10] *The Bell System Technical Journal*, Jan. 1979, p. 5.

[11] *Ibid.*, p. 7.

[12] Link interview.

[13] Dawn Stover, "Cellular Goes Digital," *Popular Science,* (January 1990), pp. 52-55.

[14] *Ibid.*, p. 53.

[15] Anthony Russo, "Bringing Cellular Down to Size," *Cellular Business*, (June 1988), p. 34.

[16] CTIA Narrow AMPS Forum, CENTEL, Chicago, IL, 9 December 1990.

[17] CTIA Winter Exposition, Gregory Vogt, *"PCN: What is it and Where is it Going,"* (Reno, Nevada, Feb. 6, 1990).

[18] Electronic Industries Association, EIA Interim Standard IS-41-A, Cellular Systems Operation, February 1990.

[19] Jessee Russell, "Technology Update," CTIA Winter Exposition, Reno, Nevada, February 6, 1990.

[20] Arunas G. Slekys, "What's Ahead Worldwide for Digital Cellular," *Mobile Radio Technology*, May 1990, p. 40.

Chapter 1

Analog Cellular

1.1. ANALOG CELLULAR INTRODUCTION

In 1971, AT&T proposed a cellular radio telephony system [1] that could meet the requirements of the FCC to serve a large number of subscribers with a limited spectrum allocation. This proposal was the backbone of the U.S. commercial cellular system that started service in Chicago, October 1983. This chapter provides a high level overview of the operation of existing Analog FM (EIA-553) equipment. Included are semi-technical descriptions and functional block diagrams. For the experienced cellular engineer, this will be a very basic description. This section explains rudimentary cellular operation for those not familiar with how it works.

1.2. SYSTEM ATTRIBUTES

The cellular system meets the original Bell System goals [2] by allowing frequency reuse, cost effective capacity expansion, and coordinated system control. Frequency reuse allows the conservative use of spectrum by using the same channels many times within one system. Capacity expansion is made possible by increasing the number of frequency channels reused. The Mobile Telephone Switching Office (MTSO) provides the central control which maintains call continuity by transferring calls from one cell to another as the user moves throughout the system (see Figure 1.1).

1.2.1. Frequency Reuse

In early mobile radio systems, one high power transmitter served a large area. This limited the total number of radio channels that could be supported within that area due to a modest authorized frequency spectrum and the bandwidth requirement for each radio. In 1976, New York City had only 12 radio channels which supported 545 subscribers with a waiting list of 3700 [3]. With limited spectrum allocation, frequency reuse is required to increase the number of radio channels within the service area. Frequency reuse is the ability for different users to transmit and receive on the same radio channel without interference because of the distance between them. As distance increases from the transmitting source, signal strength decreases exponentially. When sufficient distance has been reached from the source, the same frequency may be reused (see Figure 1.2).

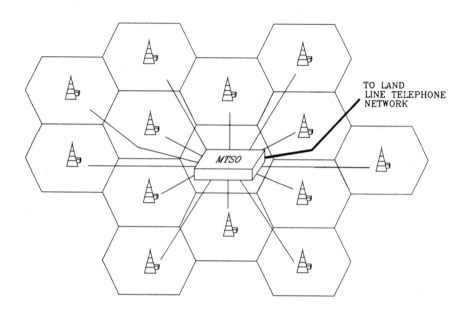

Figure 1.1 Basic Cellular System

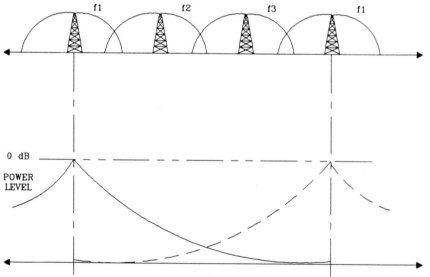

Figure 1.2 Ability to Reuse Frequencies

In the cellular system, system planners achieve a reuse of frequencies by positioning land transmitter sites that use the same radio channel at a distance to ensure low interference levels. These sites are initially planned by general RF propagation rules. Because all propagation factors cannot be accounted for, and exact locations for towers cannot always be obtained, cell site position and power levels are usually adjusted later.

1.2.2. Capacity Expansion

The technique of cell splitting allows a gradual capacity expansion. Cells are split by adding cell sites where the RF boundaries of the cell sites are changed by adjusting the power level or using directional antennas to cover a reduced area (see Figure 1.3). The boundaries of a cell site will vary with the terrain and land conditions. A significant problem is foliage. Coverage areas will actually increase in the winter when the leaves are off the trees.

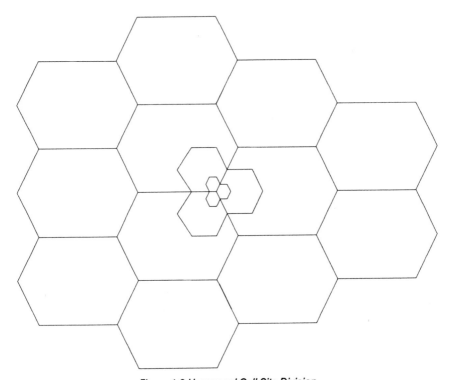

Figure 1.3 Hexagonal Cell Site Division

1.2.3. System Control

In the 1949 Detroit taxi system, communications capability was possible throughout a large service area by the reuse of frequencies. However, when moving from one service area to another, voice communications had to be reestablished by manually tuning the Mobile Station [4]. Today's cellular system maintains voice transmission when moving from one cell to another by automatic switching. The MTSO's switching equipment transfers calls from cell to cell and provides the connection of the call to other Mobile Stations or the land line telephone network. The MTSO creates and interprets the necessary command signals to control the Mobile Stations via Base Stations. This allows the switching from channel to channel as the Mobile Station moves from one coverage area to another.

1.3. SYSTEM PARAMETERS

The cellular system was developed with the technology constraints of the 1970s. Suitable frequency bands that could match cost effective equipment design were limited, the selected modulation type had to conform to a hostile mobile radio environment, and the control structure had to support large numbers of available voice channels.

1.3.1. Frequency Allocation

The goal of the FCC is to support many users with limited spectrum. In the 1970s, available spectrum was constrained to above 800 MHz [5] and due to equipment design limitations and poor radio propagation characteristics at frequencies above 1 GHz, this resulted in the allocation of the 825-890 MHz region.

In 1974, 40 MHz of spectrum was allocated for cellular service [6] and in 1986, an additional 10 MHz of spectrum was added to facilitate expansion [7]. The frequency assignment for the U.S. cellular system is 824-849 MHz and 869-894 MHz. These bands have been frequency divided (FDMA) into two 30 kHz parts per channel. This results in a maximum capacity of 832 channels. These are then divided into groups with 416 channels assigned to each system.

1.3.2. Duplex Channels

The 50 MHz allocation is divided into two 25 MHz blocks separated by 45 MHz. The Mobile Station transmits on the lower frequency band and is called the reverse channel, and the Base Station transmits on the upper frequency band which is termed the forward channel. The difference between the forward and reverse channels always remains at 45 MHz. Figure 1.4 (a) displays a Base Station transmitting to the Mobile Station at 875 MHz on the forward channel. The Mobile Station then transmits to the Base Station at 830 MHz on the reverse channel. Figure 1.4 (b) shows the Base Station transmitting at 890 MHz resulting in the Mobile Station transmitting at 845 MHz. (See Figures 1.4 (a) and (b) below.)

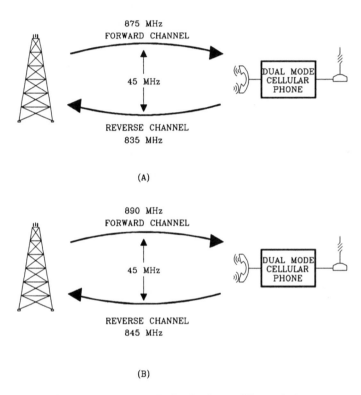

Figure 1.4 (a) and 1.4 (b) Duplex Channel Transmission

1.3.3. Modulation Type

The modulation method used is FM (Frequency Modulation) for voice and FSK (Frequency Shift Keying) for digital signaling. The modulation is optimized for the mobile environment operating at 800 MHz by using audio processing that enhances high frequency audio and minimizes transients caused by 800 MHz signal fades [8].

1.3.4. Channel Structure

In early mobile radio systems, the Mobile Station searched all the available channels until it found an unused channel. With 832 available channels, a Mobile Station could not be expected to scan all of these within a reasonable amount of time [9]. Controlling channels were established to direct the Mobile Station to an available channel. Thus, channels have been divided into controlling channels and voice channels. Of the 416 channels per system, 21 are dedicated as control channels and cannot be used as voice channels. The remaining 395 channels can be used as voice or control channels.

1.4. SYSTEM OPERATION

A cellular system consists of three basic elements: A MS (Mobile Station),[1] BS (Base Station), and MTSO (Mobile Telephone Switching Office).[2] Figure 1.1 shows a basic cellular system where the large service area is divided into smaller cells. A Mobile Station communicates by RF energy to the Base Station within its cell. The Base Station converts these radio signals for transfer to the MTSO via land line or alternate communications links. The MTSO routes the call to another Mobile Station in the system or the appropriate land line facility.

Radio channels are divided into two groups, control channels and voice[3] channels. Control channels allow the Mobile Station to retrieve system control information and compete for access. Voice channels are primarily used to transfer voice information but also can send and receive digital control messages particular to the mobile station operating on the voice channel (see Figure 1.5).

A Mobile Station initializes when first powered on by scanning the predetermined set of control channels and tuning to the strongest one. The Initialization Mode allows the Mobile Station to retrieve system identification and setup information (see Figure 1.6).

---

1   A MS is also referred to as a CSS (Cellular Subscriber Station).

2   A MTSO is also referred to as a Mobile Switching Center (MSC).

3   A voice channel carries both voice and signaling information and may also be referred to as an analog traffic channel.

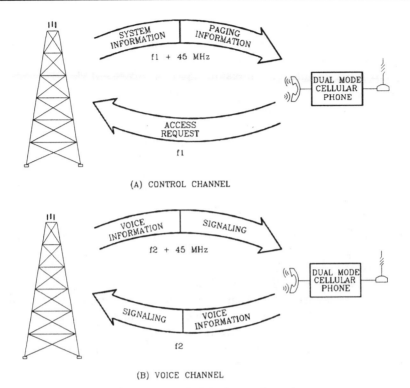

(A) CONTROL CHANNEL

(B) VOICE CHANNEL

Figure 1.5 Basic Cellular System Operation

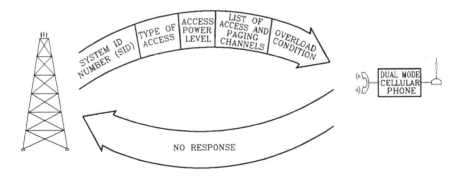

Figure 1.6 Base Station System Information

After initialization, it enters the Idle Mode where it waits for its phone number to be received (paging) or the user to originate a call (access). When a call is to be received or originated, the mobile attempts to access the system via a control channel. It enters the System Access Mode. If access is successful, the control channel sends out an IVCD (Initial Voice Channel Designation) message. The mobile tunes to the voice channel number contained in the message and enters the Conversation Mode. As the Mobile Station operates on a voice channel, the system uses FM (Frequency Modulation) which is similar to commercial FM radio broadcast stations. When control messages are required to be sent on the voice channel, a digital message replaces the voice information for a short burst (blank and burst).

1.4.1. Access

When a Mobile Station attempts to obtain service from a cellular system, it is referred to as "access." Mobile Stations compete to obtain access. Access is attempted when a command is received by the Mobile Station that indicates the system needs to service that Mobile Station (such as a call to be received) or as a result of a request from the user to originate a call. Access is performed by the Mobile Station monitoring the busy/idle status of the control channel before and during the transmission of an access attempt message. If the channel is available, it will begin to transmit while simultaneously monitoring the busy status of the control channel. The channel must become busy within the prescribed time limit or the access attempt must stop as it is assumed another Mobile Station has gained attention of the Base Station.

When an access attempt is successful, the system sends out the Initial Voice Channel Designation (IVCD) message assigning this particular Mobile Station to a cellular voice channel. If the attempt has failed, the mobile waits a random time before attempting access again (see Figure 1.7).

1.4.2. Paging

A call reaches the Mobile Station by the process of paging. A page occurs when a message is sent on the control channel which contains the Mobile Station's identification number (Phone Number) indicating a call is to be received. If the Mobile Station is active in the system and wishes to receive the call, it responds to the page by attempting access to the system (see Figure 1.8). The system knows that the type of access is a response to a page by the type of message the Mobile Station sends.

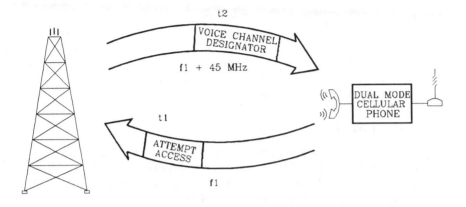

Figure 1.7 Mobile Access Attempt

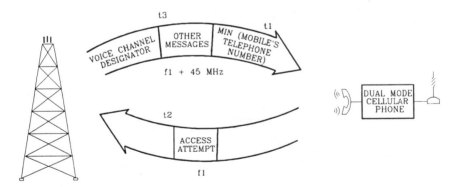

Figure 1.8 Base Station Block Diagram

1.5. FUNCTIONAL DESCRIPTION

There are three elements to a cellular system: a Mobile Station, Base Station, and MTSO. These elements are integrated to form a ubiquitous coverage radio system that can connect to the Public Switched Telephone Network (PSTN). The Mobile Station provides access between the subscriber and the cellular system. Base Stations provide the interface between the Mobile Station and the MTSO. The MTSO coordinates the operation of the cellular network and routes communications links to the PSTN.

1.6. MOBILE STATION

A Mobile Station contains a transceiver, control head, and antenna assembly (see Figure 1.9). The transceiver converts audio to RF and RF into audio. A control head provides the display and keypad which allow the subscriber to communicate commands to the transceiver. RF energy is focused and converted for transmission and reception into free space by the antenna assembly.

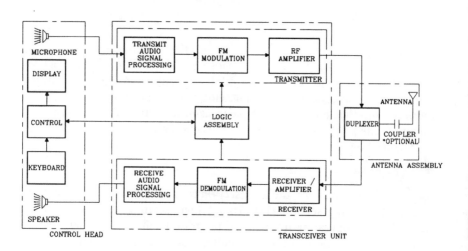

Figure 1.9 Mobile Station Block Diagram

1.6.1. Transceiver

The transceiver consists of transmitter, receiver, and logic sections. The transmitter converts low level audio signals to proportional shifts in the RF carrier frequency. The receiver amplifies and demodulates low level RF signals into their original audio form. The control section coordinates this operation by the insertion and extraction of system control messages.

1.6.1.1. Transmitter

The transmitter consists of audio processing, modulation, and RF amplifier sections. Audio processing filters the input audio signal and optimizes the changing amplitude and frequency components for FM mobile transmission [10]. The audio section also allows the combining of control signaling messages. The modulator takes the combined baseband audio signals and transforms them into proportional phase shift information at the carrier frequency. Finally, the RF amplifier boosts the output of the modulator for transmission. The transmitter is capable of adjusting its power levels to transmit only the necessary power to be received by the Base Station. To conserve battery life in portables and transportables, the RF amplifier may turn off its power periods when the mobile operator is not talking.

1.6.1.2. Receiver

The receiver consists of an RF amplifier, demodulator, and audio processing section. The RF amplifier boosts the low level RF signal to a level appropriate for input to the demodulator. The demodulator converts proportional frequency (phase) changes into audio signals. Audio processing converts audio signals optimized in the transmitter to their original frequency and amplitude levels. The receiver audio section also extracts the combined audio control signals.

1.6.1.3. Logic Section

In early applications, the logic section contained discrete logic sections for each processing section [11]. Today, logic sections usually contain a microprocessor operating from stored program memory. The logic section coordinates the operation of the transmitter and receiver section by allowing the insertion and extraction of control messages. Control signals are both analog (FM) and digital (FSK) and must be inserted into the transmitter section and extracted from the receiver section. The logic section encodes and decodes control signals and performs the call processing procedures.

1.6.2. Control Head

The control head consists of audio, display and keypad assemblies. Optional interfaces such as user data transfer, hands free, and voice activation may also be included. The control head is the interface the user operates to command the transceiver. It can be designed into the transceiver assembly to facilitate portable use.

1.6.2.1. Audio Interface

The audio interface assembly consists of a speaker and microphone. These assemblies are located in a handset although they can be replaced by units in the hands free assembly (see hands free). As in the land line system, a sidetone is generated to allow users the capability to hear from the speaker what they are saying into the microphone.

1.6.2.2. Display

The display assembly allows for pre-originating dialing [12]. The number is displayed as dialed and may be altered before the call is initiated. An IN USE symbol is displayed when the call is initiated, indicating that RF power is being transmitted. The display may also indicate other available features such as an RSSI (Received Signal Strength Indicator), call timer, or other services.

1.6.2.3. Keypad

The keypad allows the user to enter information to control the phone. This includes dialed numbers and commands to receive and originate calls. The keypad may sometimes be replaced by voice activation (see 1.5.1.2.6, voice activation).

1.6.2.4. Hands Free

For safety reasons, the phone may have an option allowing the subscriber to use hands free operation [13]. A hands free system consists of: a speaker, usually located in the cradle assembly; a remote microphone, usually located near the visor; and interface circuitry which connects the audio paths and allows for sensing when the user requests hands free mode.

1.6.2.5. User Data Transfer

The control head can offer optional connections for a facsimile, modem, or a standard Plain Old Telephone Service (POTS) to the cellular phone. On the PSTN network, voice or data information can be sent reliably if it is within the 300-3000 Hz frequency range. While the audio frequency range on the cellular radio channel is the same as the PSTN, the varying nature of the RF channel is not well suited for efficient standard data transfer. Special error correction modems exist to increase the reliability and efficiency of data transfer via the cellular system [14].

A standard telephone interface may also allow a cellular phone to operate with a touch tone or rotary phone [15]. The interface simulates a dial tone and a call is initiated without the requirement of pre-origination dialing.

1.6.2.6. Voice Activation

Another optional feature includes voice activation which allows calls to be dialed and controlled by voice commands. It is recommended a call should not be dialed by a handset while driving [16], but a call can be initiated via voice activation without significant distraction.

Two types of speech recognition exist – speaker dependent and speaker independent. Speaker dependent requires the user to store his voice command to be associated with particular commands. These recorded commands are used to match words spoken during operation. Speaker independent allows multiple users to control the phone without the recording of a particular voice. To prevent accidental operation of the Mobile Station by words in normal conversation, key words such as "Phone Start" are used to indicate a voice command [17].

1.6.3. Antenna Assembly

An antenna provides two essential functions. It matches the impedance of the transceiver to that of free space, and it focuses the transmission into a desired direction [18]. A Mobile Station antenna assembly consists of an antenna, cabling, duplexer, and possibly a coupling device for antenna connection through glass. The choice of an antenna system and mounting location can enhance or reduce the performance of the Mobile Station. The antenna may be an integral part of the transceiver section or externally mounted. Antennas can have a gain where energy is focused into a beamwidth area. This focused energy gives the ability to communicate over greater distances, but as the angle of the antenna changes, the direction of the beam also changes, reducing performance. For example, car-mounted antennas that have been tilted to match the style lines of the automobile, often result in extremely poor performance.

Cabling adds losses which reduce the performance of the antenna assembly. High gain antennas may be used to overcome these losses and possibly allow for a lower power output [19].

In early systems, separate antennas were used for transmitters and receivers. A duplexer allows one antenna to serve both the transmitter and receiver. It consists of two RF filters – one for transmission and one for reception. Glass mount antennas permit the mounting of an antenna without requiring a hole although poor ground planes associated with these antennas may result in poor performance (see chapter 2).

1.6.4. Base Station

A Base Station consists of transceivers, control sections, RF combiner, communications links, scanning receiver, backup power supplies, and an antenna assembly (see Figure 1.10). The transceiver sections are similar to the Mobile Station transceiver as they convert audio to RF signals and RF to audio signals. The control sections coordinate the overall operation of the Base Station. The RF combiner allows the separation of radio channels between a multiple of transceivers and antenna assembly. Communications links route audio and control information between the Base Station and MTSO. A scanning receiver provides the capability of measuring the signal strength on any of the cellular channels. The backup power supply maintains operation when primary power is interrupted. Many of the sections within the Base Station will be duplicated in the event of equipment failure.

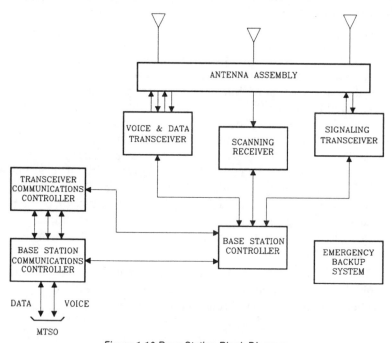

Figure 1.10 Base Station Block Diagram

1.6.4.1. Transceivers

Base Station transceivers have the same functional elements as a Mobile Station: a transmitter, receiver, and logic sections. Each transceiver section provides for one communication channel. The transmitter section converts audio from a communications link to RF for transmission to the Mobile Station. The receiver section converts RF received from the Mobile Station to audio for routing via a communications link. A logic section inserts and extracts signaling information under command of the controller section. Unlike the Mobile Station, the transmit, receive, and logic sections are grouped into equipment racks. For example, a single equipment rack may contain all of the RF amplifiers. An additional transceiver per Base Station is dedicated for a signaling channel.

Transmitter

A Base Station transmitter has audio processing, modulation, and an RF power amplifier. An audio processing section converts the audio (often in digital form) from the communications link to the optimized frequency and audio levels (see Mobile Station audio processing) for FM modulation. The transmitter audio section also allows the insertion of control information. A modulation section converts these audio signals into proportional phase shifts at the carrier frequency. The RF power amplifier boosts this signal to a much higher power than the Mobile Station (possibly 100 Watts) and normally does not change output power.[4]

Receiver

The receiver sections in the Base Station consist of an RF amplifier, demodulator, and audio processing sections. The RF amplifier boosts the low level signals for appropriate amplitude for input to the demodulator and usually provides for diversity reception (see Base Station Antenna Assembly). The demodulator converts the RF to audio signals. Audio processing converts the optimized audio to its original frequency and amplitude levels. Receiver audio processing also extracts control information and converts the output audio level for transmission on the communications link.

---

4   A feature now offered by manufacturers allows for the reduction of power to reduce co-channel interference. This is referred to as dynamic power control.

Logic

The logic section of the Base Station consists of control signal routing and message processing. Audio and digital signaling messages are inserted and extracted from the radio channel on command of the controller section. Digital messages are encoded and decoded from the logic section.

1.6.4.2. Controller

There are three types of controllers: base station controller, base station communications controller, and transceiver communications controller. The base station controller coordinates the operation of all Base Station equipment based on commands received from the MTSO. Voice and Data communications from the MTSO are buffered and rate adapted by the base station communications controller. Digital voice information is converted to analog and routed to the radios by the transceiver communications controller. Controllers provide for the insertion of control channel signaling messages, setup of voice channels, and operation of the scanning receiver. In addition, controllers monitor equipment status and provide operational and failure status to the MTSO.

1.6.4.3. RF Combiner

Narrow bandpass filters in the RF combiner allow separate transmitters with different frequency outputs to be connected to the same antenna assembly without significant interference. This is accomplished by the coupler (bandpass filter) being tuned to its associated transmitter. The output power of the transmitter can be passed through the filter, but other transmitter outputs at different frequencies are unable to pass through.

1.6.4.4. Communications Links

Communications links carry both data and voice information. Options for the links include hard wire, microwave, or fiber optic. Communications links are often digital time multiplexed T1 (see chapter 3, T1) to increase the efficiency of the line. To prevent a single link failure from disabling communications, alternate communications should be provided [20].

1.6.4.5. Antenna Assembly

In a start-up cellular system, Base Station antenna assemblies usually employ omni-directional antennas [21]. As the system matures, directional antennas replace the original antennas for reduced interference and sectoring. Separate transmit and receive antennas are used. Two receive antennas are used for diversity reception which allows the selection of one of multiple antennas with a stronger receive signal strength to minimize the effects of Rayleigh fading.

Mobile Station owners have been reluctant to place more than one cellular antenna on the car which has limited the use of diversity reception [22] by subscribers. Diversity reception is almost always used in Base Station reception.

1.6.4.6. Scanning Receiver

A scanning receiver[5] is used to provide signal strength measurement for potential handoff channels. It is capable of tuning to any channel and measuring the received signal strength. It determines the relative distance a Mobile Station is from the Base Station by measuring its received signal strength. When the signal strength falls below an acceptable level, the Base Station signals the MTSO that a handoff will be necessary. Commands are also received from the MTSO to tune the scanning receiver to a particular channel so signal strengths at several Base Stations can be compared to determine the best handoff decision.

1.6.4.7. Backup Energy Sources

In 1989, a hurricane in Puerto Rico destroyed all land line communications. Due to good planning, cellular communications were unaffected and became the primary communications link [23]. To permit operation of a base station when primary power is no longer available, backup energy sources are required. Backup energy sources are needed to supply equipment power and operate cooling systems.

1.6.5. Mobile Telephone Switching Office

The MTSO consists of controllers, switching assembly, communications links, operator terminal, subscriber database, and backup energy sources (see Fig. 1.11). The controllers are the brains of the entire cellular system, guiding the MTSO through the creation and interpretation of commands to and from the Base Stations. A switching assembly routes voice connections from the Base Stations to the PSTN land lines. Communications links may be a variety of copper wire, microwave, or fiber optic mediums. An operator terminal allows supervision and maintenance of the system. A subscriber database contains customer specified features and billing records. Backup energy

---

5   A scanning receiver is also known as a locating receiver.

sources provide power when primary power is interrupted. As with the Base Station, the MTSO has duplication of circuits and backup energy sources to allow system operation to be maintained when a failure occurs.

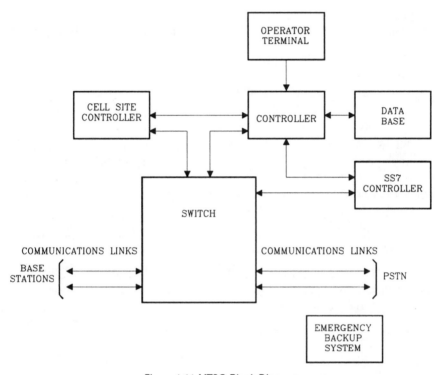

Figure 1.11 MTSO Block Diagram

1.6.5.1. Controller

Controllers provide for coordination of Base Stations, MTSO switching functions, and PSTN connections. A cell cite controller creates and interprets commands to and from the Base Station. The cell controller commands the MTSO switch, validates customers requesting the system, maintains billing records from both airtime and PSTN usage, and monitors for equipment failures. Communications controllers process and buffer voice and data information between the MTSO, Base Stations, and PSTN [24].

1.6.5.2. Switching Assembly

The switching assembly allows connections between Base Station links and PSTN links. This may be a physical connection or a logical path (digital). Early switches were analog and required a physical connection between switch paths. Almost all cellular switches are digital and have a much higher efficiency [25].

1.6.5.3. Communications Links

Communications links contain both data and voice paths. Typically, there are alternate communications links that are not routed through the same network points. This allows the reconfiguring of the links when one or more of the circuits has failed or is unavailable. A majority of communications use a T1 Time Division Multiplex (TDM) Pulse Coded Modulation (PCM) digital transmission (see chapter 3, T1 links).

1.6.5.4. Operator Terminal

While operation is performed by the controller, maintenance and administrative functions are accomplished by data terminals which consist of a display device and keyboard. Maintenance operator terminals allow for diagnostics and fault isolation. Administrative operator terminals allow the entry and extraction of subscriber database information.

1.6.5.5. Subscriber Database

The subscriber database maintains a customer base on a Mobile Identification Number (MIN) and Electronic Serial Number (ESN). Each customer has a user profile which includes selected long distance carrier, calling restrictions, service fee charge rates, and other network options. This database allows billing records to be maintained.

1.6.5.6. Backup Energy Sources

As with the Base Station, when primary power is interrupted, backup energy sources are needed to operate the cellular system. Backup energy sources include batteries and diesel generators which are used to supply equipments and cooling systems. The current draw on the backup energy sources may exceed the typical primary power current as disaster situations increase the demand for wireless communications [26].

1.7. SUMMARY

The main objective of cellular is to provide radio telephony to many users. This is accomplished by frequency reuse, cost effective capacity expansion, and coordinated system control. Key parameters of cellular include a limited frequency allocation of 50 MHz, use of FM modulation, and separate control and voice channels.

A cellular system has three main elements: a Mobile Station (MS), Base Station (BS), and Mobile Telephone Switching Office (MTSO). The MS links the subscriber to the Base Station via FM radio transmission. Base Stations convert signals from Mobile Stations to signals that are relayed to the MTSO. The MTSO connects the cellular call to the land line network or other mobiles via BS equipment.

A MS contains a transceiver, control head, and antenna assembly. These elements may be integrated together to form a portable Mobile Station. The transceiver converts audio to RF and RF to audio. A control head provides the user with status display information and the ability to command the MS via a keypad or voice activation. An antenna assembly converts RF between the transceiver and electromagnetic waves propagated in free space.

Base stations contain transceivers, control sections, RF combiners, communications links, scanning receiver, backup power supplies, and antenna assemblies. Several transceivers are provided for voice channels and one is dedicated for a controlling channel. Control sections interpret, create, and buffer command and voice information. RF combiners allow the sharing of an antenna assembly by a plurality of transmitters and receivers. Communications links transport voice and data information between the BS and MTSO. A scanning receiver measures the strength of the MS signal which enables the determination of handoff possibility. Backup power supplies enable the BS to operate during interruption in primary power. Antenna assemblies are used to convert and direct RF energy between BS equipment and free space electromagnetic waves.

The MTSO consists of controllers, switching assembly, communications links, operator terminals, subscriber database, and backup energy sources. MTSO controllers coordinate all the elements of the cellular system. A cell site controller directs BS equipment, a call controller performs administrative functions, and a communications controller transforms and buffers voice and data information among the MTSO, Base Stations, and Public Switched Telephone Network (PSTN). The switching assembly routes calls between Base Stations and the PSTN. Communications links transport voice and data via copper wire, microwave, or fiber optic mediums. Operator terminals allow administrative and maintenance information to be observed and entered into the MTSO system. A subscriber database contains billing and subscriber preference information. Backup energy sources allow for operation of the cellular system when primary power is interrupted.

References:

[1] Dr. George Calhoun, *Digital Cellular Radio*, (MA: Artech House, 1988),pp.50-51.

[2] American Telephóne and Telegraph Company, *The Bell System Technical Journal* (Murray Hill, New Jersey), January 1979, Vol. 58, No. 1, pp.9-10.

[3] William Lee, *Mobile Cellular Telecommunications Systems* (McGraw Hill, 1989) , p. 2.

[4] James Craig, "Dispatching a Large Taxi System," *Communication Engineering,* (October 1953), pp. 20-21.

[5] Calhoun, p. 46.

[6] Lee, p. 5.

[7] *Ibid.*, p. 265.

[8] *The Bell System Technical Journal,* Jan. 1979, pp. 110-114.

[9] *Ibid.*, p. 50.

[10] *Ibid.*, p. 110.

[11] *Ibid.*, p. 139.

[12] *Ibid.*, pp. 148-49.

[13] CTIA Winter Exposition, "Safety," San Diego, February 17, 1991.

[14] U.S. Patent 4,697,281, "Cellular Telephone Data Communication System and Method," Harry M. O'Sullivan, 1987.

[15] U.S. Patent 4,658,096, "System for Interfacing a Standard Telephone Set with a Radio Transceiver," William L. West Jr. and James E. Shafer, 1987.

[16] CTIA, Winter Exposition, "Safety," San Diego, 1991.

[17] U.S. Patent 4,827,520, "Voice Actuated Control System for Use in a Vehicle," Mark Zeinstra, 1989.

[18] William Sinnema, *Electronic Transmission Technology*, (Prentice Hall 1979), pp. 201-204.

[19] "Why Cellular Mobiles Use 'High-Gain' Antennas," *Mobile Radio Technology* (MRT) editorial staff, Vol. 5, Issue 5, May 1987, pp. 44-46.

[20] CTIA, Winter Exposition, "Disaster Experiences," Reno, Nevada, February 6, 1990.

[21] Lee, p. 160.

[22] Calhoun, p. 243.

[23] CTIA Winter Exposition, "Disaster Experiences," Reno, Nevada, February 6, 1990.

[24] U.S. Patent 4,887,265, Packet-Switched Cellular Telephone System, Kenneth Felix, Dec. 1989.

[25] Lee, p. 327.

[26] CTIA, "Disaster Experiences."

Chapter 2

Analog Mobile Station

2.1. ANALOG MOBILE STATION INTRODUCTION

To establish communications in a cellular system, Analog Mobile Stations must operate within electrical parameters, conform to signaling structures, and call process signaling messages. The analog mobile station contains functional sections to comply with these requirements. This chapter provides a technical description of mobile station parameters, signaling structures, call processing, and functional assemblies.

2.2. ANALOG MOBILE STATION PARAMETERS

Mobile Stations must conform to EIA-553 [1] and IS-19B [2] to ensure compatibility with the cellular system network. These standards contain parameters for the RF channel structure, signaling and call processing functions. RF transmission and reception occurs in the 800 MHz region and uses FM modulation. Signaling uses the RF channel to send and receive messages. These messages are then processed by the call processing algorithms for Mobile Station control.

An analog Mobile Station must operate within the given constraints of the cellular system. It must operate at any of the cellular channel frequencies, have a controllable power output, and use FM modulation.

2.2.1. Channel Frequency Assignment

The frequency range of the Mobile Station transmitter is from 824 to 849 MHz, commonly referred to as the reverse channels. The frequency of the Mobile Station receiver is from 869 to 894 MHz and is known as the forward channels. Each channel is allocated two (2) 30 kHz bands that are separated by 45 MHz. A specific channel frequency is determined by the following formula:

reverse channel:

1 to 799	$0.03(N) + 825.0$ MHz
990 to 1023	$0.03(N-1023) + 825.0$ MHz

forward channel

1 to 799	$0.03(N) + 870.0$ MHz
990 to 1023	$0.03(N-1023) + 870.0$ MHz

To allow competition (and reduced regulation) cellular channels were divided to support 2 operators per regional area. One set of channels would be assigned to a wireline provider and the second set to a non-wireline.[1] The wireline carrier is defined to be the "B" carrier and the non-wireline is the "A" carrier. See Figure 2.1.

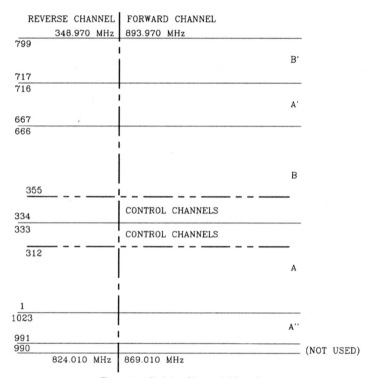

Figure 2.1 Cellular Channel Allocation

2.2.2. Mobile Station Power Output

Mobiles are classified by power output capabilities. A class I mobile is capable of 6 dBW (3 Watts), class II 2 dBW (1.6 Watts), and class III (portables) -2 dBW (.6 watts). Class III portables are necessary for safety reasons where portable phones are limited to a maximum radiated power that

---

1   A wireline carrier is a company that also provides land line telephone service.

is incident on the user. Mobile Station power output is adjusted by commands received from the Base Station to allow reduced emissions from the mobile in the smaller cells.

2.2.3. Modulation

RF Modulation is a method used to convert information contained by the audio signal to the radio channel. This transports the information more effectively. The modulation input signal contains the information to be transmitted and is referred to as the baseband signal. The RF carrier, or broadband signal, transports the information.

Amplitude Modulation

The simplest form of modulation is amplitude modulation. When a radio frequency is generated, its amplitude is varied in proportion to the modulating signal. See Figure 2.2.

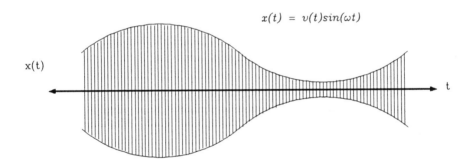

$$x(t) = v(t)sin(\omega t)$$

Figure 2.2 Amplitude Modulation

Frequency Modulation

In 1936, Armstrong demonstrated a transmission method that overcame some of the limitations of Amplitude Modulation (AM). Frequency Modulation (FM) was not as susceptible to noise and varying channel conditions [3]. Information contained in an FM signal is contained in the varying offset frequency of the carrier signal. For FM, without modulation input, the output is a constant carrier frequency (wc). As the audio (information) signal is applied to the modulator, the carrier frequency is offset in proportion to the amplitude of the information signal. The maximum amount of offset the carrier can be shifted above or below the reference is called the peak deviation. Generally, + and - peak deviations are equal. See Figure 2.3.

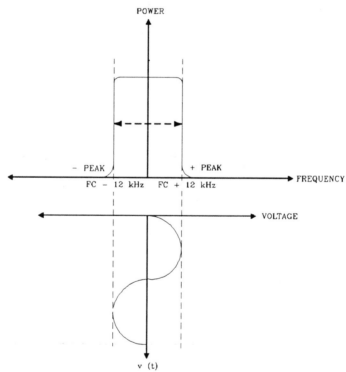

Figure 2.3 Frequency Modulation

A simple table may help illustrate frequency modulation. In this sample table, a carrier frequency 45.0 MHz is offset by +/- 10 kHz. If +/- 5 volts is the maximum input allowed to the modulator, we have a 10 kHz peak deviation. See Table 2.1.

Table 2.1 Frequency Modulation

Input (volts)	Output (MHz)	Deviation
0.0	45.0	0.0 kHz
1.0	45.002	2.0 kHz
2.0	45.004	4.0 kHz
5.0	45.010	10.0 kHz
-1.0	44.998	-2.0 kHz
-2.0	44.996	-4.0 kHz
-5.0	44.990	-10.0 kHz

The base band (audio) signal input to the modulator is optimized so RF channel impairments are minimized [4]. This includes companding and expanding, preemphasis and deemphasis, and audio bandpass filtering.

2.2.4. RF Channel Structure

There are two types of channels for a cellular system. One group is dedicated as control channels and the other is voice channels. Control channels transfer system overhead information and coordinate access to voice channels. Voice channels allow the user to transport information (usually voice) through to other users.

For the A service provider, control channels are 313 to 333 and for the B service provider, control channels are 334 to 354. Control channels cannot be used for voice channels although some voice channels can be assigned as control channels.

A control channel provides three basic functions: sending system overhead information, paging information, and access control. System overhead information consists of parameter information unique to a system and is continuously sent to Mobile Stations operating within that system. Paging is a process where messages are directed toward a particular Mobile Station to alert it to an incoming call. Access control provides for contention resolution of Mobile Stations randomly competing for service from a Base Station.

A voice channel is used to transport user information, usually voice information, by the use of FM modulation. Control on a voice channel is accomplished by digital messages which, when sent, inhibit voice transmission for a limited period of time.

2.3. SIGNALING

Given the physical RF channel parameters, a Mobile Station communicates with the cellular system by sending signaling messages. Signaling message formats vary between control channels and voice channels. Control channel signaling is all digital and voice channel signaling is a mixture of digital messages and audio tones.

2.3.1. Control Channel Signaling

Information is transferred on the control channel by FSK (Frequency Shift Keying). The data transmission rate is 10 kbps. It is Manchester-encoded to allow self-synchronization [5]. Orders are sent as messages, and a message is composed of one or more words.

A dotting sequence of alternating 1s and 0s are used as an indication that a message will begin. The alternating of bits produces a strong 5 kHz frequency component which is easily detected [6]. A synchronization word follows the dotting sequence which defines the exact starting point of the coming message. Message words follow the dotting and synchronization words. Because the radio channel is subject to signal strength fades and errors, message words are repeated 5 times to ensure reliable reception. Of the five repeats, a majority vote of 3 out of 5 words are used to eliminate the recognition of corrupted messages. See Figure 2.4.

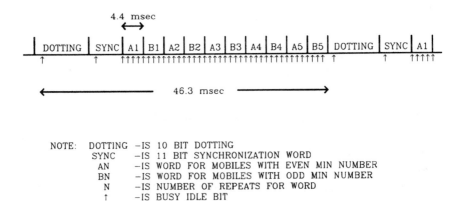

NOTE:
DOTTING —IS 10 BIT DOTTING
SYNC —IS 11 BIT SYNCHRONIZATION WORD
AN —IS WORD FOR MOBILES WITH EVEN MIN NUMBER
BN —IS WORD FOR MOBILES WITH ODD MIN NUMBER
N —IS NUMBER OF REPEATS FOR WORD
↑ —IS BUSY IDLE BIT

Figure 2.4 Signaling on the Forward Control Channel

Message and signaling formats on the control channels vary between forward and reverse channels. The forward channel is a synchronous channel and the reverse channel is asynchronous.

2.3.1.1. Forward Control Channel

For the forward control channel, 10 words follow a dotting/sync word sequence. Words are alternated A,B,A,B,etc. where A words are designated for mobile units with an even phone number and B words are designated for mobiles with odd phone numbers.

A forward channel word is 40 bits. Each word has BCH error correction/detection included so the data content is 28 bits and parity is 12 bits. The forward channel is interleaved with Busy/Idle (B/I) bits which indicates the serving capacity of the Base Station.

2.3.1.2. Reverse Control Channel

For the reverse channel, 5 words follow the dotting sequence. A reverse channel word is 48 bits and each word has BCH error correction/detection included so the data content is 36 bits and parity is 12 bits. Messages are sent on the reverse channel as coordinated using the Busy/Idle bits from the forward control channel. See Figure 2.5.

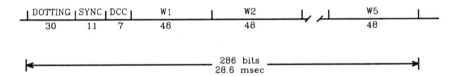

```
NOTE: DOTTING  -IS 30 BIT DOTTING SEQUENCE
        SYNC   -IS SYNCHRONIZATION WORD
         DCC   -IS DIGITAL COLOR CODE
          WN   -IS MESSAGE WORD
           N   -IS NUMBER OF REPEATED MESSAGE WORDS
```

Figure 2.5 Signaling on the Reverse Channel

2.3.2. Voice Channel Signaling

While the analog voice channel[2] is used to pass user information (usually voice information) between the Mobile Station and the Base Station, signaling information must also be sent to provide physical layer control. Signaling on the voice channel can be divided into in-band and out-of-band signaling. In-band signaling occurs when audio signals between 300-3000 Hz either replace or occur simultaneous with voice information. Out-of-band signaling information is composed of signals above or below the 300-3000 Hz range and may be transferred without alteration of the voice information.

Signals sent on the voice channel include Supervisory Audio Tone (SAT), Signaling Tone (ST), Dual Tone Multi-Frequency (DTMF), and blank and burst FSK digital messages.

2.3.2.1. Supervisory Audio Tone

The SAT tone ensures maintenance of a reliable transmission path between the mobile and Base Station. The transmission of an SAT tone occurs simultaneously with the voice and provides an indication of a closed loop. This is similar to a land line telephone where a current/voltage is sensed indicating a phone is off hook [7]. The SAT tone may be one of the three frequencies: 5970,6000,6030 Hz. The system designates which frequency is to be used by the DCC (Digital Color Code) received in the control channel overhead message train. A loss of SAT implies the channel conditions have become impaired and if long enough (approximately 5 seconds) the call must be terminated.

SAT is also used to identify co-channel interference. If an interfering signal is of a sufficient level to interfere with the Mobile Station, the received SAT frequency will be different than the one designated by the DCC. If the received signal has an incorrect SAT code, the audio is muted so the operator will not hear another mobile's conversation.

An alternate use of the retransmission of SAT is position location. By comparing the phase relationship of the transmitted SAT tone to the received SAT tone, an approximate propagation time can be calculated. This propagation time is correlated to the distance from the Base Station. Due to

---

2 The Analog Voice channel transports both voice and digital signaling information and is commonly referred to as an Analog Traffic Channel.

multipath propagation, the accuracy of this location feature has been poor and has not been very useful [8]. Only the retransmission of SAT as a pilot tone is critical to operation.

2.3.2.2. Signaling Tone

The Signaling Tone (ST) is a 10 kHz tone burst and is used to indicate a status change. It confirms messages sent from the Base Station and is similar to a land line phone status change of going on or off hook.

2.3.2.3. Dual Tone Multi Frequency (DTMF)

Touch-tone (registered trademark of AT&T) signals (DTMF) may be sent over the voice channel. DTMF signals are used to retrieve answering machine messages, direct automated PBX systems to extensions, and a variety of other control functions. Bellcore specifies frequency, amplitude, and minimum tone duration for recognition of DTMF tones [9]. While transmission of DTMF tones can be accomplished on the voice channel, varying channel conditions can alter the expected results. In poor radio conditions and a fading environment, the radio path may be interrupted for short periods of time. This results in the possibility of recognition of a multiple of digits when only one key was depressed.

2.3.2.4. Blank and Burst Messages

When signaling data is to be sent on the voice channel, audio FM signals are inhibited and replaced with digital messages. The bit rate for messages is 10 kbps and is transmitted by FSK (Frequency Shift Keying). Similar to the control channel signaling structure, messages are repeated a multiple of times and a majority vote is taken to see which messages will be used.

To inform the receiver that a digital signaling message is coming, a 101 bit dotting sequence which produces a 5 kHz tone precedes the message. After the dotting sequence is transmitted, a synchronization word follows which depicts the exact start of the message.

Blank and burst signaling on the voice channel differs between the forward and reverse direction. On the forward voice channel, messages are repeated 11 times to ensure control information is correctly received even in poor radio conditions. On the reverse voice channel, words are repeated only 5 times. Words on the forward voice channel contain 40 bits and on the reverse voice channel contain 48 bits. Both types of words have 12 bits of BCH error detect/correct parity.

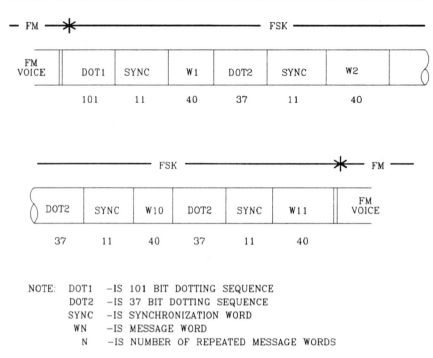

NOTE: DOT1 – IS 101 BIT DOTTING SEQUENCE
      DOT2 – IS 37 BIT DOTTING SEQUENCE
      SYNC – IS SYNCHRONIZATION WORD
        WN – IS MESSAGE WORD
         N – IS NUMBER OF REPEATED MESSAGE WORDS

Figure 2.6 Signaling on the Forward Voice Channel

2.4. CALL PROCESSING

Signaling is the method used to transfer messages. Call Processing executes the command messages sent. A given sequence of processing for signaling messages must exist for a Mobile Station to correctly operate within a system. Functional operations are divided into four tasks: initialization, idle, access, and conversation. A task is a sequence of operations the mobile must accomplish to fill a functional requirement. The Mobile Station must first complete the Initialization task to obtain system parameters. It then remains in the Idle task where it waits for new system information, pages, or the operator to initiate a call. Once a call is initiated or is to be received, the Mobile Station enters the System Access task where it competes for assignment to a voice channel. Once the system has assigned a voice channel, the Mobile Station enters the Conversation task.

In addition to sequential tasks, other functions occur in parallel. Timers are set and continuously monitored to permit Mobile Station operation. In the event of a failure of one of these timers, the Mobile Station must be inhibited from transmitting.

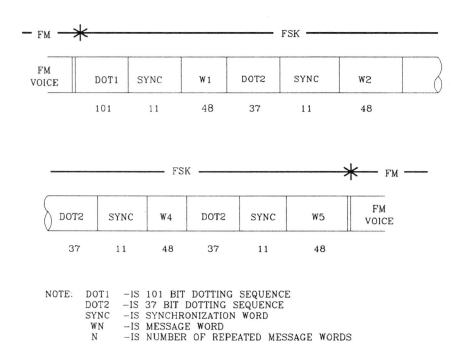

NOTE: DOT1 —IS 101 BIT DOTTING SEQUENCE
       DOT2 —IS 37 BIT DOTTING SEQUENCE
       SYNC —IS SYNCHRONIZATION WORD
       WN   —IS MESSAGE WORD
       N   —IS NUMBER OF REPEATED MESSAGE WORDS

Figure 2.7 Signaling on the Reverse Voice Channel

2.4.1. Initialization

System overhead information is continuously sent on the control channels to allow Mobile Stations to obtain parameters necessary to establish communication and inform the operator of the status of the Cellular System. When the Mobile Station is first turned on, it scans a group of dedicated control channels and locks onto the strongest signal. It then transfers system parameters from information contained in the overhead messages to the memory of the Mobile Station such as SID (System Identification), number of paging channels, and ROAM status. See Figure 2.8.

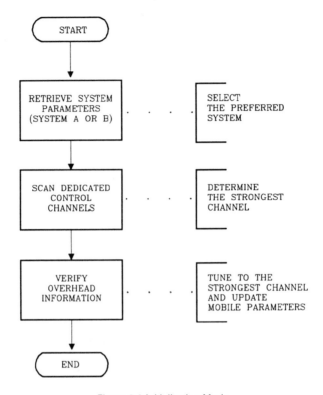

Figure 2.8 Initialization Mode

2.4.2. Idle Mode

When the Mobile Station has obtained the system parameters, it must monitor the overhead messages for changes in the parameters, obtain its pages, and determine if a call is to be initiated. Overhead messages include system ID (used for ROAM status), number of access channels, and other parameters which affect how the mobile will operate. Page commands are monitored to determine if an incoming call is to be received. The Mobile Station also monitors the status of its control head to see if the user has initiated a call. See Figure 2.9.

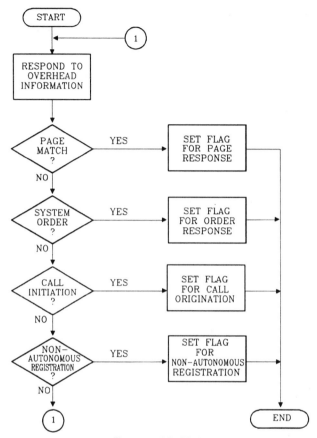

Figure 2.9 Idle Mode

2.4.3. System Access

While the control channel provides system and control information to the Mobile Station, it also provides an access point for the mobile when the system needs to be serviced. Mobile Stations attempting access on the cellular network is a random event. To prevent mobiles from initiating access simultaneously, a seizure collision avoidance procedure has been developed. The contention resolution process can be divided into four features: busy status of channel, random time delays, system response time interval, and maximum number of automatic access attempts.

The forward control channel is interleaved with dedicated bits that indicate if the Base Station is busy. Before attempting access to the system, the mobile will monitor these bits and wait until they indicate the Base Station is not busy. See Figure 2.10.

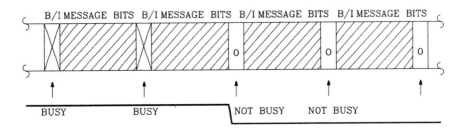

Figure 2.10 Busy Idle Bit Stream

When the Mobile Station attempts access, the control channel should indicate busy within a prescribed time because it is serving the accessing mobile. If the channel becomes busy before or after the time period, the Mobile Station assumes the Base Station is responding to a competing Mobile Station unit and must inhibit transmission.

If a Mobile Station has attempted access and was not successful, it must wait a random time before attempting access again. This prevents repeated access attempts at the same time from two or more competing mobiles.

The number of automatic attempts is limited to a maximum number to prohibit the continual overloading of a system by many mobiles consistently attempting to access the system.

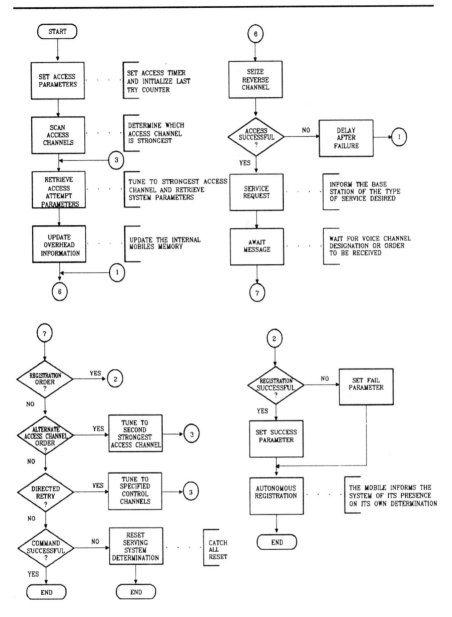

Figure 2.11 Access Mode

When the mobile receives a page, orders, registration request, or the operator initiates a call, the mobile attempts to gain access to the system. The access attempt contains a message that indicates what type of access is required. The Base Station may also send a registration request which requires the Mobile Station to respond indicating it is operational within the system. Registration requests are sent to limit the paging requirements by knowing that a mobile is active in a particular cell area.

Control channels may be divided into separate paging and access channels where one control channel delivers pages and a different control channel coordinates access. This method was created to allow access channels to handle the increased service requests independent of paging requirements. Separate paging and access channels have not turned out to be very beneficial as all the access signaling occurs on the forward channel and all paging occurs on the reverse channel and separating their functions into two separate channels does not increase system capacity.[3] For this reason, paging and access control are usually combined on one control channel.

2.4.4. Conversation

Access is granted when a voice channel is assigned by an Initial Voice Channel Designation (IVCD) message. The message includes a voice channel number for which the Mobile Station must tune to initiate conversation. The Base Station continues to control the Mobile Station while conversation is in progress. Many other tasks are performed which include: power level control, handoff, alerting, etc. This is accomplished with blank and burst signaling where the voice information is inhibited and replaced with signaling commands. The duration of the signaling commands are short, so disruption of the voice is not noticed.

To ensure a reliable radio link, a radio link timer is used to detect the loss of radio continuity. This timer monitors SAT and is set to 5 seconds. If allowed to expire, it indicates the radio link could not be maintained. This timer ensures that when the Mobile Station receive signal falls below an acceptable level, it must turn itself off as the mobile cannot be controlled by the Base Station.

---

3 Another application of separate paging and access channels allows an increased efficiency by reversing the paging and access functions. This is covered in chapter 5.

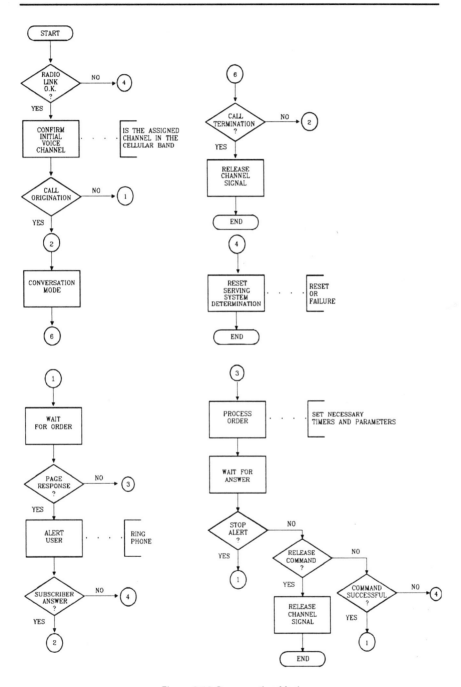

Figure 2.12 Conversation Mode

An additional feature that may become operable while in the conversation mode, particularly in portable Mobile Stations, is Discontinuous Transmission (DTX). To conserve transmitted power, transmission from the Mobile Station may be turned off[4] during silent speech intervals[5] during the conversation task.

2.5. ANALOG MOBILE STATION DETAILED DESCRIPTION

The Mobile Station consists of three elements: A transceiver section, antenna section, and control head. While these elements may all be incorporated into one portable unit, the functional entities remain the same. The transceiver converts audio to RF and RF to audio signals, the antenna assembly transforms energy to and from free space propagation, and the control head allows the operator to command the unit.

The block diagram shown in figure 2.13 is of a specific implementation. While the blocks may differ between manufacturers, the functional elements of each block must be performed.

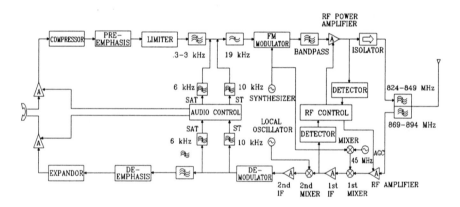

Figure 2.13 Mobile Station Block Diagram

---

4   The power level may be reduced and not completely turned off.

5   DTX is an optional feature that is not provided by all cellular systems.

2.5.1. Transceiver

The transceiver consists of transmitter, receiver, and logic sections. The transmitter converts low level audio signals to proportional shifts in the carrier frequency and provides for amplification of this RF signal. The receiver amplifies and demodulates low level RF signals into their original audio form. The logic section coordinates this operation by the insertion and extraction of system control messages.

2.5.1.1. Transmitter

The transmitter section processes audio signals into a frequency modulated RF carrier. The transmitter consists of preemphasis, compandor, bandpass filter, limiter, signal combiner, modulator, mixer, synthesizer, RF amplifier, and isolator sections.

Preemphasis

The preemphasis section optimizes the frequency components of the audio signals for FM transmission. Speech audio signals contain most of their energy at the low frequencies. Thus, the signal to noise ratio of the higher frequencies is lower. The signal to noise ratio of high frequency components is further degraded as the noise output of the demodulator increases exponentially at higher frequencies. Therefore the noise output of the demodulator is highest where the audio signal frequency components are the smallest [10].

The preemphasis section is used to increase the high frequency components of the audio signal to overcome this problem. This section is matched by a deemphasis section in the receiver which restores the frequency components to their original level.

Compandor

The compandor compresses the dynamic range of the audio so speakers with different voice intensities have approximately the same amplitude level. A quiet speaker will cause a much smaller mean deviation than a loud speaker. This would result in a lower perceived transmission quality for soft speakers [11].

Bandpass Filter

The bandpass filter limits the input frequencies to the audio band of 300 to 3000 Hz. This filter band limits speech signals so that out-of-band speech energy does not influence the gain of the compressor or affect the gain of the amplitude limiter [12].

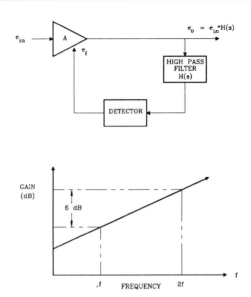

Figure 2.14 Preemphasis Block Diagram and Response Curve

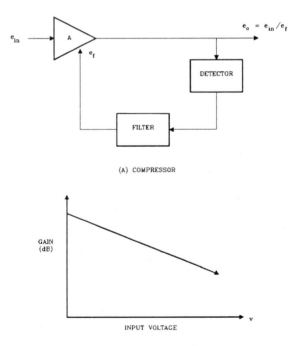

Figure 2.15 Compandor Block Diagram and Response Curve

Amplitude Limiter

A limiter is required to keep the FM modulator from emitting RF energy outside the allotted bandwidth when the input speech levels are excessive [13]. If the user could overmodulate the transmitter, this could interfere with mobiles in adjacent cells.

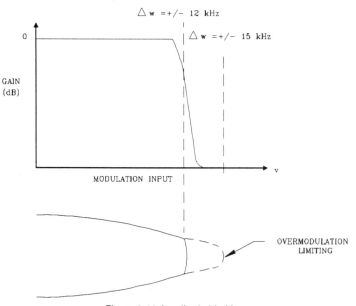

Figure 2.16 Amplitude Limiting

Signal Combining Section

The signal combining section allows insertion of SAT and ST control tones into the audio path. The SAT and ST are supplied to the modulator after the audio band pass filter because they are outside the frequency range of the filter.

Phase Modulator

The phase modulator converts a voltage level input to a proportional frequency shift of the carrier signal. The FM carrier is set to a maximum of +/- 12 kHz peak deviation which is less than the +/- 15 kHz allotted bandwidth. The phase modulator is also used to FSK (Frequency Shift Keying) modulate the RF carrier when digital messages are transmitted.

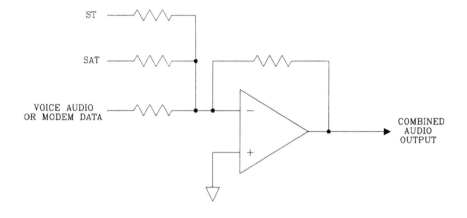

Figure 2.17 Audio Control Summer

Synthesizer

The frequency synthesizer generates any one of 832 stable carriers upon direction from the microprocessor in the logic section. A frequency synthesizer is composed of a Voltage Controlled Oscillator (VCO), reference oscillator, programmable frequency divider, and Phase Locked Loop (PLL) [14].

A VCO is an oscillator assembly that adjusts its frequency in proportion to an input voltage. A reference oscillator is supplied to a programmable frequency divider (counter) which divides a high input frequency to output pulses at the desired frequency. These pulses are compared in phase to the VCO by the PLL, and the error voltage created in proportion to the phase difference. This error voltage is used to fine tune the VCO until it matches the exact frequency of the output of the frequency divider.

Transmitter Mixer

A mixer is a non-linear device that performs frequency conversion by hetrodyning two input signals at different frequencies to a third frequency different from the first two. FM modulation is often performed at a low frequency then the transmitter mixer hetrodynes this low frequency modulator and synthesizer outputs to the carrier frequency of the RF channel.

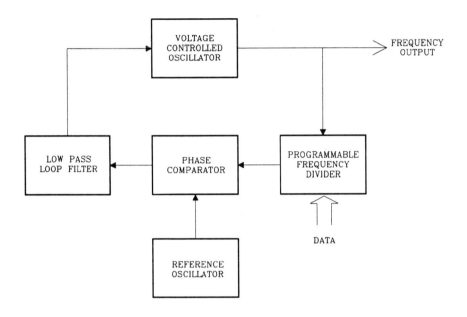

Figure 2.18 Frequency Synthesizer Block Diagram

RF Amplifier

The RF amplifier must be capable of adjusting its output level as a result of commands sent by the Base Station. This is necessary so the Mobile Station RF output power does not interfere with other cell sites or overdrive the cell site receiver.

The RF amplifier must be capable of providing RF energy much in excess of the class use of equipment to overcome the transmission losses of filtering and isolation. Typically, if the RF output of a mobile, class I, is capable of 3 watts, the RF amplifier will be capable of providing 6 watts.

The RF amplifier must include a fail safe protection circuit that will inhibit transmission if any section of the mobile fails. This is accomplished by a timer circuit that must be continuously reset by functioning circuits or transmission is gated off.

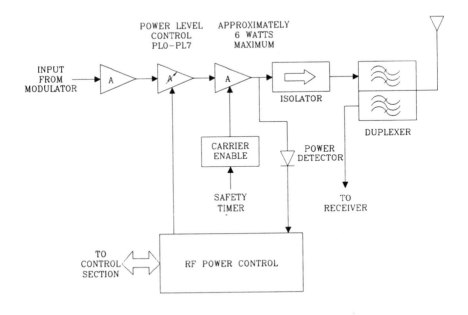

Figure 2.19 RF Amplifier Section

RF Band Pass Filter

An additional RF band pass filter is required to ensure RF components outside the allotted channel bandwidth are attenuated. The spectral mask in figure 2.20 shows the maximum allowable transmit bandwidth. If this bandwidth is exceeded, interference to other Mobile Stations and Base Stations may occur.

Isolator

The output of the RF amplifier is passed through an isolator which permits energy to flow in one direction and absorbs energy traveling in the opposite direction. An isolator is required to prevent damage to the RF section which could occur as a result of poor antenna impedance matching (see 2.5.2.4. Antenna). Isolators typically have a 0.4 dB insertion loss in the forward direction and greater than 10 dB loss in the reverse direction [15].

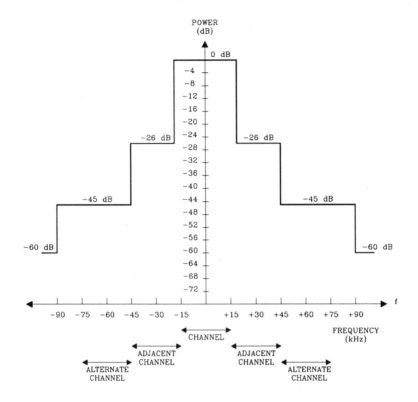

Figure 2.20 RF Bandpass Spectral Mask

2.5.1.2. Receiver

The receiver section processes low level RF broadband signals into their original audio components. The purpose of the receive section is to only pass the desired bandwidth of signal and to amplify that signal to a workable level. It consists of receiver amplifier section, Automatic Gain Control (AGC), IF amplifiers, mixer sections, demodulator, and audio signal processing.

Receiver RF Amplifier Section

A sensitive receiver requires an RF amplifier so that the received signal that may be in the order of picowatts (-116 dBm) is increased to the workable range of the mixer section. The receiver amplifier is a broad band RF amplifier which has a variable gain controlled by the AGC.

Automatic Gain Control (AGC)

The AGC compensates for a large dynamic range of the received signal strength level which is approximately 70 dB. The workable range of the mixer section is smaller than the received signal dynamic range. As the received signal increases, the gain of the RF amplifier is reduced to maintain a relatively constant input to the mixer section.

1st Receiver Mixer

The 1st receiver mixer superheterodynes[6] the received RF signal with another oscillator source to produce a lower Intermediate Frequency (IF). The main advantage is the oscillator source may be varied so the IF is a constant frequency simplifying RF amplifier design and tuning [16]. For the cellular transceiver, one input to the 1st receiver mixer is a variable oscillator and the other is the received RF signal. Because the frequency synthesizer adjusts for each RF transmit channel and is a constant 45 MHz difference from the receive frequency, the variable oscillator input typically is the frequency synthesizer mixed with another fixed frequency oscillator. When mixed with the received RF signal, this results in a constant frequency output.

1st Intermediate Frequency Amplifier

The function of the 1st intermediate frequency (IF) amplifier is to selectively amplify the difference frequency signal developed in the 1st receiver mixer section. The IF section consists of amplifiers and fixed tuned sections which accept signals within a desired band of frequencies while rejecting others. The band pass characteristics of this section determines the freedom from interference as well as the fidelity of the receiver [17].

2nd Receiver Mixer

The 2nd receiver mixer superheterodynes the first IF with another oscillator source to produce a much lower frequency than the first IF (Intermediate Frequency).[7]

2nd Intermediate Frequency Amplifier

The function of the 2nd intermediate frequency (IF) amplifier is to selectively amplify the difference frequency signal developed in the 2nd receiver mixer section. The 2nd IF amplifier section consists of amplifiers and fixed tuned sections which accept signals within a desired band of frequencies

---

6   If the heterodyning process results in an intermediate frequency that is not the original baseband frequency, it is referred to as superheterodyning.

7   The second IF frequency is typically 455 kHz.

while rejecting others. The main advantage to the 2nd IF is the narrow bandwidth filters that can be used at this lower frequency. The band pass characteristics of this section further determines the freedom from interference as well as the fidelity of the receiver.

FM Demodulator

The FM demodulator changes frequency shifts to proportional voltage changes. There are a number of methods used to demodulate the audio intelligence from the FM waveform. Perhaps the simplest method uses a discriminator or slope detector where the FM signal is applied to a slightly off tune resonant circuit. As the IF signal varies along the slope of the bandpass of the resonant circuit, this results in a varying amplitude signal in proportion to the offset in reference frequency. This amplitude is then detected by a peak detector similar to those used in AM signals [18].

An indirect demodulation method uses a Phase Locked Loop (PLL) as described in the frequency synthesizer section. The PLL compares the phase of a received frequency and generates an offset voltage which changes a Voltage Controlled Oscillator (VCO) to match the exact frequency. If a phase locked loop is applied to the IF amplifier section, the control voltage to the VCO contains the demodulation information as it is proportional to the frequency deviation from a reference frequency [19].

Audio Signal Separator

Audio control signals are extracted by a group of filters which direct frequency components of the audio signal to be routed to separate processing sections. This is accomplished by the use of band pass filters with their center frequency fixed around 6 kHz for SAT and 10 kHz for the ST.

An audio band pass filter eliminates all other signals from entering the receiver audio processing section of the receiver as its bandpass range is from 300 to 3000 Hz. Control signals would effect the operation of the deemphasis and expandor sections if permitted to enter the receive audio processing section.

Deemphasis

The deemphasis section reverses the effects of the transmitter preemphasis section. In this section, rapid transients such as channel noise are eliminated. The deemphasis section is an integrator which lowers the gain for the high frequency components while permitting low frequency signals to pass unaffected. Use of a preemphasis/deemphasis combination improves the performance in the presence of channel impairments, primarily the clicks that are inherent in the transmission in a moving vehicle at the 850 MHz band [20].

Expandor

The expandor section reverses the effects of the transmitter compressor section. In this section, amplitude changes are expanded (amplified) to increase the dynamic range of the audio signals. The expandor section provides additional gain for high amplitude components while permitting low amplitude components to pass unaffected.

2.5.1.3. Logic Section

The original AT&T prototype used an INTEL 8080 microprocessor, 5K-bytes of stored program memory, and dedicated logic circuits [21]. Many of the original AT&T channel decoding circuits did not use the microprocessor due to timing or coding restraints. Today, the logic section microprocessor uses stored program control where a program stored in memory operates the transceiver. There are four types of memories used in a transceiver: Electrically Erasable Programmable Read Only Memory (E^2PROM), [Erasable] Programmable Read Only Memory ([E]PROM), Read Only Memory (ROM), and Random Access Memory (RAM). E^2PROMs can have information written to, read from, and can be erased electrically although E^2PROMS cannot be written to many times and are slow in the writing cycle. EPROMs can be written to, read from, and erased but must be erased by an ultraviolet light. PROMS can be written to and read from, but only can be programmed one time. ROM has information stored in physical links stored at the manufacturing facility and can only be read from. RAM can be written to and read from rapidly, but loses information when power is removed.

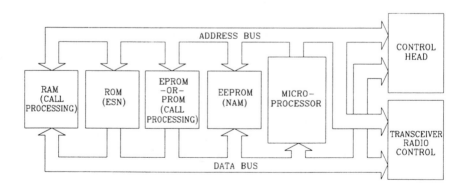

Figure 2.21 Logic Section Block Diagram

E^{2}PROMs are used to store data such as NAM information and other slow changing long term information. EPROMS or PROMs hold the stored programs for call processing. ROMs hold permanent data that cannot be changed such as the Electronic Serial Number (ESN). RAM is storage for data temporarily saved during call processing.

Figure 2.21 shows a logic section configuration where a microprocessor is controlled by memory devices and interfaces to the Control Head and Transceiver radio devices. Of key significance is a programmable memory section reserved for user specific information. The Number Assignment Module (NAM) section contains information about the unit's telephone number, class of service, and optional features. This information must be programmed into the Mobile Station before it can be placed into operation.

2.5.2. Antenna Assembly

A Mobile Station antenna assembly consists of a duplexer, cabling, optional coupling device, and antenna. The proper selection, and location of the antenna system is critical to the performance of the Mobile Station.

2.5.2.1. Duplexer

Although usually mounted in the transceiver assembly, the duplexer enables one antenna to serve the transmitter and receiver assemblies. The duplexer consists of two band pass filters tied to one common antenna. One band pass filter is for the receive frequency range (869-894 MHz), the other is for the transmit frequency range (824-849 MHz). Duplexers add a loss to the transmitted and received signal of approximately 1dB (25%).

2.5.2.2. Cabling

Cable losses can be significant when the antenna is mounted far from the transceiver. Typical losses of .2 dB per foot can be expected [22]. This results in a 2 dB loss (63%) for a 10 foot cable.

2.5.2.3. Coupler

Energy can be radiated through glass by a capacitive coupling device. While absorption through glass is not significant, couplers may introduce loss by not providing an effective ground plane or not providing a good match. This mismatch discussed in the following Antenna section results in coupler transmissionlosses.

2.5.2.4.Antenna

The antenna may be an integral part of the transceiver or externally mounted. The antenna transforms RF energy from the transceiver into electromagnetic waves for transmission in free space. The antenna must match the impedance of the source[8] to the impedance of free space to transfer the maximum power available. When a mismatch occurs, some of the energy is not radiated and is reflected back into the transmitter assembly. The Standing Wave Ratio (SWR) is a measure of the ability of the antenna to match its specified impedance.

$$VSWR = \frac{1 + \frac{VReflected}{VForward}}{1 - \frac{VReflected}{VForward}}$$

If it is a perfect match:

$$VSWR = \frac{1 + 0}{1 - 0} = 1:1$$

Anything but a perfect match results in an SWR of greater than one.

When measuring power with a wattmeter:

$$SWR = \frac{1 + \sqrt{\frac{PReflected}{PForward}}}{1 - \sqrt{\frac{PReflected}{PForward}}}$$

For example, an antenna that has 10% of its power reflected back:

$$SWR = \frac{1 + \sqrt{0.1}}{1 - \sqrt{0.1}} = \frac{1 + .316}{1 - .316} = \frac{1.316}{.684} = 1.9:1$$

Most cellular antennas require a ground plane where a metal base must exist for efficient transmission. This results in challenges for mounting on cars fabricated with nonmetallic materials such as the Corvette. In addition, the location of the antenna on the ground plane will effect the antenna pattern [23].

---

8 An ideal match occurs with the complex conjugate impedance.

An antenna may perform directivity where transmitted energy is focused into a beamwidth resulting in a transmission gain. This works well in Mobile Stations in vehicles where a focused beam height varies little. Unfortunately, the beam direction is influenced by the relative angle of the antenna to the groundplane. For antennas that are tilted, energy is focused in the wrong direction which results in poor transmission and reception. High gain antennas have also shown to increase fading and have a lesser gain in suburban environments [24].

2.5.3. Control Head

The control head consists of a display, keypad, audio interface, and interconnect cabling. The control head is the interface between the user and the cellular system as the user may enter commands and observe the response of the Mobile Station.

2.5.3.1. Interface Cabling

Connection between the control head and the transceiver unit requires cabling.[9] The original specification for cellular phones mandated a standard interface cable that contained dedicated test line connections [25]. The elimination of an interface standard requirement in EIA-553 has resulted in the reduction in size and number of conductors from 16 to 8 in the interconnect cabling.[10]

2.5.3.2. Display

A display readout should be provided which displays user-entered digits. The display also provides the user with status information on the operation of the Mobile Station. The display should provide the following indicators: NO SERVICE, ROAM, IN USE, LOCK, and HORN ALERT (optional). Back lighting should be provided for night operation [26]. While the display was required in the original AMPS specification, the ability to interface to a Plain Old Telephone System (POTS) allows for the operation without a display [27].

---

9   Portable cellular transceivers may have the control head integrated into the unit eliminating the interface cabling.

10   The Audiovox CTX-3200A uses 8 conductors, other manufacturers may use more or less.

2.5.3.3. Keypad

The keypad allows the user to enter information to control the phone. The original AMPS specification contained physical parameters such as size, key force, contact bounce, illumination, key travel distance, and color. Size and spacing should be sufficient to prevent accidental operation of the adjacent keys. It is recommended that the keys be translucent and light in color with dark labeling. Key travel distance should be between .4 and 2.5 mm. Key force should be between 200 and 450 grams. Contact bounce should be limited to 10 msec. Back lighting should be provided for night operation [28].

2.5.3.4. Audio Interface

The audio interface typically consists of a speaker and microphone mounted in a handset. Hands free operation may be provided to allow the use of microphone and speaker assemblies mounted in an alternate location. When hands free operation is in use, some of the received signal is echoed back into the microphone resulting in feedback (a squeal). To reduce this feedback, Voice Controlled Switching (VCS) is usually employed where the receive speaker volume is reduced when an operator is speaking.

2.6. SUMMARY

A Mobile Station must conform to industry standards to ensure compatibility with the cellular system. Key system parameters include channel frequency assignment, power output, modulation type, and RF channel structure.

The Mobile Station communicates with the cellular system by sending signaling messages. Signaling messages on the control channels are digital and are transferred by Frequency Shift Keying (FSK). Control channels have busy/idle bits interleaved in the signaling messages which allow the Mobile Station to sense when the system is busy prior to attempting system access. Voice channel signaling is a combination of FM audio and FSK digital messages. A Supervisory Audio Tone (SAT) is mixed with the voice information to indicate a continuous link and differentiate between interfering signals. Digital messages on the voice channel are sent using a blank and burst method where audio signals are inhibited for a short period of time while the digital messages are transmitted.

Mobile Station operation can be divided into four modes. When a Mobile Station is first turned on, it performs the initialization mode by tuning to the strongest control channel and extracting system overhead information.

It then remains in the idle mode where it continues to update system information and waits for a call to be originated or received. When access to the system is required, the Mobile Station continuously monitors the busy status of the control channel and attempts access by sending a message indicating what type of access is required. Conversation mode is entered and voice information may now be transferred.

The Analog Mobile Station consists of three sections: a transceiver section, antenna section, and control head. The transceiver converts audio to RF and RF to audio. The antenna assembly transforms energy to and from free space propagation. A control head allows the operator to command the Mobile Station.

References:

[1] Electronic Industries Association, EIA-553, "Mobile Station - Land Station Compatibility Specification" (1990).

[2] Electronic Industries Association, EIA Interim Standard IS-19-B, Recommended Minimum Standards for 800 MHz Cellular Subscriber Units (May 1988).

[3] Gary M. Miller, *Modern Electronic Communication*, pp. 154-167, Prentice Hall, New Jersey (1988).

[4] American Telephone and Telegraph Company, *The Bell System Technical Journal,* (Murray Hill, New Jersey), January 1979, Vol. 58, No. 1, pp. 110-14.

[5] *Ibid.*, p. 98.

[6] *Ibid.*, pp. 114-115.

[7] *Ibid.*, p. 47.

[8] Personal Interview, Ron Bohaychuk, Ericsson Radio Systems, 7 October 1990.

[9] Bellcore, "LSSGR; Signaling, Section 6," TR-TSY-000506, Rev 1, December, 1988.

[10] Ferrel G. Stremler, *Introduction to Communication Systems*, (Addison-Wesley, 2nd edition, 1982), pp. 337-339.

[11] *The Bell System Technical Journal,* Jan. 1979, p. 110.

[12] *Ibid.*, p. 113.

[13] *Ibid.*, p. 108.

[14] Edward Singer, *Land Mobile Radio Systems,* (Prentice Hall, New Jersey, 1989), pp. 62-64.

[15] Gary M. Miller, *Modern Electronic Communication*, (Prentice Hall, New Jersey, 1988), pp. 568-570.

[16] L.J. Giacoletto, *Electronic Designers Handbook*, (McGraw-Hill, 2nd edition, 1977), pp. 23-24.

[17] Alexander Schure, *Superheterodyne Converters and I-F Amplifiers*, (John F. Rider Publisher, 1956), p. 29.

[18] Stremler, pp. 315-319.

[19] *Ibid.*, pp. 315-316.

[20] *The Bell System Technical Journal*, Jan. 1979, p. 103.

[21] *Ibid.*, pp. 137-139.

[22] William Sinnema, *Electronic Transmission Technology*, (Prentice Hall, 1979), p. 11.

[23] D.W. Horn, *"Vehicle-Caused Pattern Distortion at 800 MHz,"* pp. 197-200, (IEEE 1983 Vehicular Technology Conference).

[24] John Belrose, *"Vehicular Antennas for 800 MHz Mobile Radio,"* pp. 191-197, (IEEE 1983 Vehicular Technology Conference).

[25] Advanced Mobile Phone Service, Inc., *"Cellular Mobile Telephone Equipment Specification,"* pp. 1.2-3 (1983).

[26] *Ibid.*, pp. 2.3-1, 2.3-2.

[27] U.S. Patent 4,658,096, "System for Interfacing a Standard Telephone Set with a Radio Transceiver," William L. West Jr. and James E. Shafer, 1987.

[28] *"Cellular Mobile Telephone Equipment Specification,"* pp. 2.3-1, 2.3-2.

Chapter 3
Analog Cellular System Network

3.1. INTRODUCTION

Unlike cellular's predecessor, Improved Mobile Telephone Service (IMTS), cellular is an integration of radio technology and network intelligence [1]. The cellular system network is composed of Base Stations, a Mobile Telephone Switching Office (MTSO), communication links, and PSTN interconnection. This chapter describes these basic network elements, their technical characteristics, operation, and the cellular system planning process.

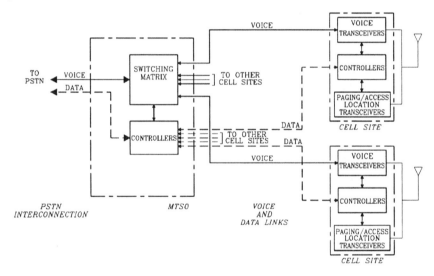

Figure 3.1 System Network Block Diagram

3.2. ANALOG BASE STATION

A Base Station provides multiple-channel transmitting and receiving facilities for a cell site area. To provide a standard RF communications link between the Base Station and Mobile Stations, Base Stations must operate within electrical parameters, conform to signaling structures, and call process signaling messages. The analog Base Station contains functional sections to comply with these requirements.

3.2.1. Base Station Parameters

Base Stations must operate in conformance with EIA-553 [2] and IS-20A [3] to ensure interoperability with Mobile Stations. These standards contain the specific parameters for the RF channel frequency assignment, power output, modulation, and channel structure.

3.2.1.1. Channel Frequency Assignment

The frequency range of the Base Station receiver channels is from 824 to 849 MHz, and they are termed reverse channels. The frequency range of the Base Station transmitter channels is from 869 to 894 MHz, and they are called forward channels. Each voice channel is allocated two (2) 30 kHz bands that are separated by 45 MHz. A specific channel frequency is determined by the following formula:

reverse channel:

$$1 \text{ to } 799 = 0.03(N) + 825.0 \text{ MHz}$$
$$990 \text{ to } 1023 = 0.03(N\text{-}1023) + 825.0 \text{ MHz}$$

forward channel:

$$1 \text{ to } 799 = 0.03(N) + 870.0 \text{ MHz}$$
$$990 \text{ to } 1023 = 0.03(N - 23) + 870.0 \text{ MHz}$$

Channel frequencies for Base Stations are selected by a frequency plan (see table 3.1) to not interfere with other cell site areas. Once assigned, these channels are rarely changed.[1]

---

[1] An optional new feature allows for dynamic channel allocation where the fixed set of Base Station channel frequencies can be varied as the number of users increases in a particular cell site area.

Table 3.1 Sample Cellular System Frequency Plan

Channel Group	B1	B2	B3	B4	B5	B6	B7	B8	B9	B10	B11	B12	B13	B14	B15	B16	B17	B18	B19	B20	B21
Control	334	335	336	337	338	339	340	341	342	343	344	345	346	347	348	349	350	351	352	353	354
Channel	355	356	357	358	359	360	361	362	363	364	365	366	367	368	369	370	371	372	373	374	375
	376	377	378	379	380	381	382	383	384	385	386	387	388	389	390	391	392	393	394	395	396
	397	398	399	400	401	402	403	404	405	406	407	408	409	410	411	412	413	414	415	416	417
	418	419	420	421	422	423	424	425	426	427	428	429	430	431	432	433	434	435	436	437	438
	439	440	441	442	443	444	445	446	447	448	449	450	451	452	453	454	455	456	457	458	459
	460	461	462	463	464	465	466	467	468	469	470	471	472	473	474	475	476	477	478	479	480
	481	482	483	484	485	486	487	488	489	490	491	492	493	494	495	496	497	498	499	500	501
	502	503	504	505	506	507	508	509	510	511	512	513	514	515	516	517	518	519	520	521	522
	523	524	525	526	527	528	529	530	531	532	533	534	535	536	537	538	539	540	541	542	543
	544	545	546	547	548	549	550	551	552	553	554	555	556	557	558	559	560	561	562	563	564
	565	566	567	568	569	570	571	572	573	574	575	576	577	578	579	580	581	582	583	584	585
	586	587	588	589	590	591	592	593	594	595	596	597	598	599	600	601	602	603	604	605	606
	607	608	609	610	611	612	613	614	615	616	617	618	619	620	621	622	623	624	625	626	627
	628	629	630	631	632	633	634	635	636	637	638	639	640	641	642	643	644	645	646	647	648
	649	650	651	652	653	654	655	656	657	658	659	660	661	662	663	664	665	666	—	—	—

3.2.1.2. Base Station RF Power Output

Typically, the maximum Effective Radiated Power (ERP) for MSA systems is 100 Watts and RSA systems is 500 Watts [4]. The limiting factor in a cellular system is the power available from the Mobile Station, not the maximum power available from the Base Station. This is becoming a complex problem with the continued demand for portable cellular phones that can receive the high power Base Station signal. Because they can only return a 600 mWatt signal to the base station, this system results in the land line party having poor voice quality.[2]

---

2 Some implementations of base stations may include high gain antennas and tuned cavities for receive channels which increases the sensitivity of the base station receivers.

3.2.1.3. Channel Structure

Two types of channels are needed for a cellular system. One type is dedicated as control channels and the other is voice channels. An omni directional Base Station will have one dedicated control channel[3] and several voice channels. The control channel transfers system overhead information and coordinates access to voice channels. Voice channels allow the user to transport information (usually voice) through to the MTSO.

3.2.2. Base Station Operation

The Base Station receives RF signals from Mobile Stations within its particular service area, converts the RF signals to voice and data information, and transfers this information to the MTSO via communication links. Base Station operation involves signaling, call processing, maintenance, and diagnostics. Signaling transfers messages between the RF channel (Mobile Station) and the communications links (MTSO). Call processing interprets and processes messages for Mobile Station control via the Base Station. Maintenance allows for the transfer of performance data from the BS to MTSO to monitor the status of BS equipment. Diagnostics allow for equipment component failure fault isolation.

3.2.2.1. Signaling

Signaling associated with the base station has two parts. The first part is the signaling between the MTSO and the Base Station Controller (BSC). The second part is the signaling between the Base Station and the Mobile Station.

Signaling between the MTSO and BSC occurs on a communications circuit dedicated as a data link. For the early cellular application, this was a separate dedicated phone line [5]. Cellular systems today often use one of the 24 multiplexed channels on a T1 link (see 3.4 T1 communications) as the control data channel.

Signaling between the BS and MS on the RF channel is the same as described in 2.3. Some signaling commands created by the MTSO are passed through the Base Station directly to the MS. Other commands are created by the BS controller. Signaling to the MS via RF on the control channel is accomplished by FSK signaling. Signaling on the voice channel is accomplished by a combination of FM and FSK.

---

3   A Base Station that has been divided into sectors may have a dedicated control channel for each sector.

3.2.2.2. Call Processing

A Base Station is used to translate voice information between a communication link and an RF channel, monitor the signal strength of any channel that a mobile station is operating on, and send and receive control information to the MS.

Call processing for a BS can be divided into control of the MS and control of the BS. The BS must translate MS commands that are created by the MTSO, and also interpret commands from the MTSO that are equipment control commands for the base station.

The Base Station controls the MS by the sending of digital and audio signaling messages on the RF channel. Some of these messages are created at the MTSO and some are originated by the Base Station. Mobile Station control information includes system overhead information, power level, and channel frequency assignment.

BS equipment control commands include equipment operational setup (for scanning receiver control), maintenance status, and equipment reconfiguration (for diagnostics).

3.2.2.3. Maintenance

Base station status is continuously sent to the MTSO to indicate if all equipment is operational. When equipment fails, the BS can reconfigure spare equipment (if it is equipped) to continue service. Maintenance tasks include routine testing functions used to detect possible faults before they affect subscriber service. Routine test functions operate in a background mode and are suspended when a fault has been detected. Diagnostics begin and status reports may be continuously printed to inform operators.

Test signals may be inserted to monitor the operational status of equipment. Loop back testing inserts test signals on one path of a system and monitors the response of the test signals on a return path. Figure 3.2 shows two loop back test paths. First, an audio test signal is inserted on a voice link sent from the MTSO to the cell site. This test signal is returned on another voice path to the MTSO via the 4 wire line card. If the signal is not successfully returned, the fault can be isolated to one of the two voice links or the 4 wire line card interface. A second loop back test validates the RF transmission equipment. The test audio signal is directed to the transmission and reception equipment. Prior to transmission on the antenna section, a portion of the output signal is sampled, shifted in frequency by 45 MHz, and redirected to the receiver sections. If the test signal is received by the MTSO, the RF transmission and reception equipment are known to be in good operating status. Other loop back paths may be created to further isolate other network equipment.

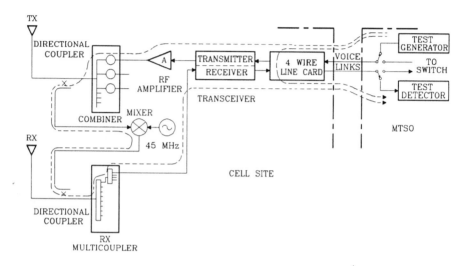

Figure 3.2 Maintenance Loop Back Testing

3.2.2.4. Diagnostics

Diagnostics commands sent from the MTSO are used to isolate discovered faults. Diagnostics can be divided into two levels. First level diagnostics isolate a faulty section and reconfigure standby equipment to continue service. Second level diagnostics fault, isolate, restore operation, and verify the restore process [6].

3.2.3. Analog Base Station Detailed Description

The Base Station consists of a control section, transceivers, RF amplifiers, receiver multicoupler, RF combiner, communication processors, scanning receiver, power supplies, and an antenna assembly. A control section coordinates the overall operation of the Base Station. The transceiver sections are similar to the Mobile Station transceiver sections as they convert audio to RF signals and RF to audio signals. RF amplifiers boost the output of the transceivers so enough RF energy can cover the designated cell site area. Receiver multicouplers split the received RF signals to allow connection to all its associated Base Station receivers. The RF combiner allows the merging of radio channels from a multiple of transceivers to one antenna assembly. Communications processors translate audio and control information between the BS and MTSO. The scanning receiver provides the capability of measuring the signal strength on any of the cellular channels. The power supply provides operating voltages and backup systems to maintain operation when primary power is interrupted. Many of the sections within the Base Station will be duplicated in the event of equipment failure. Figure 3.3 shows a Base Station block diagram.

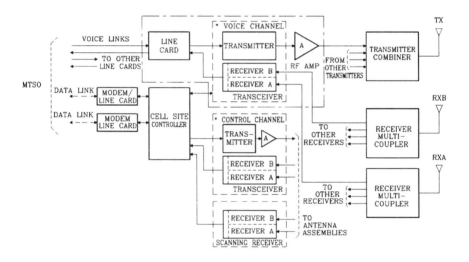

Figure 3.3 Analog Base Station Block Diagram

3.2.3.1. Controller

The controller coordinates the operation of the BS equipment through its own stored program control and based on commands received from the MTSO. The controller consists of stored program memory, microprocessor, and interface circuitry which allows control of BS equipment. The controller call processes messages, commands voice and control transceivers, and provides for maintenance and diagnostic functions.

3.2.3.2. Transceivers

The Base Station transceiver sections have similar transmitter, receiver, and logic processing sections as the Mobile Station (see 2.5). A Base Station transmitter has audio processing, modulation, and RF power amplifier. The receiver frequently has the capability of diversity reception which requires dual RF amplifier, demodulator, and audio processing sections (see figure 3.4). The logic section of the Base Station consists of control signal routing which inserts and extracts audio and digital signaling messages from the radio channel.

Unlike the Mobile Station, these equipment sections may be physically separate and located with other transceiver sections of a similar type. For example, a single equipment rack may contain all of the RF amplifiers.

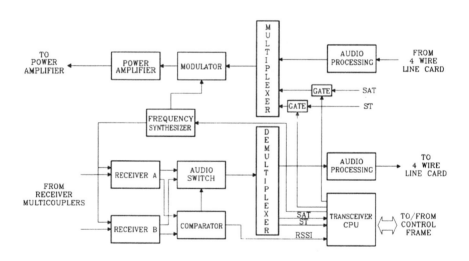

Figure 3.4 Base Station Transceiver with Diversity Reception

3.2.3.3. RF Power Amplifier

Base Station transmitters are usually set to a much higher power than the Mobile Station and rarely change output power.[4] A power amplifier unit is provided for each transceiver to increase its transmitter output power.[5] A class C RF amplifier may be used for high efficiency as FM modulation does not require linear amplification. Directional couplers are used to measure the forward and reflected power for maintenance and diagnostic functions.

3.2.3.4. RF Multicoupler

A receiver multicoupler is provided for each receive antenna to allow a single antenna to serve several receivers (see figure 3.5). The splitting of the received signal reduces its total available power. By increasing the number of receivers, the signal to noise ratio to each receiver section is reduced. Often, low noise RF preamplifiers are included to boost the low level received signals prior to the RF multicoupler splitter.

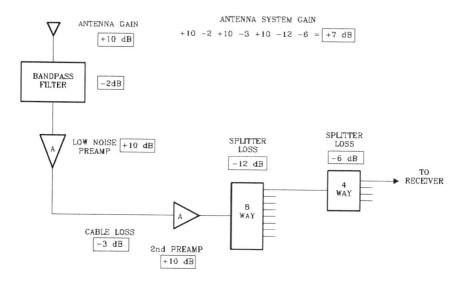

Figure 3.5 RF Multicoupler Block Diagram

---

4   Some implementations of base stations include high gain antennas which reduce the need for an RF amplifier.

5   The AT&T Series II base stations use one linear amplifier for all channels.

3.2.3.5. RF Combiner

The RF combiner is similar to the duplexer where an antenna is shared between several devices operating on different frequencies (see figure 3.6). The output of each RF amplifier is passed through an isolator, through a tuned cavity, and connected to the transmit antenna assembly. Isolators permit power to enter the combiner section from an RF amplifier and attenuates reflected power from leaving the combiner section to protect the RF amplifier section. The tuned cavity provides low attenuation at its operating frequency and high attenuation at other frequencies which prohibits signals from entering other RF amplifier sections.

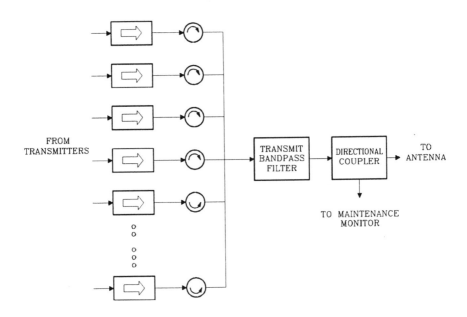

Figure 3.6 RF Combiner Section Block Diagram

3.2.3.6. Communications Link Processor

The Base Station must be capable of interfacing to a communications link for the transfer of voice and data information to the MTSO. Communication links transfer information by landline, fiber, or microwave. The function of the communications link processor is to convert the audio (baseband) signals between the Base Station equipment to a format suitable for transfer via communication links. Figure 3.7 (a) shows how the received audio from the transceivers may be converted to digital format.

Audio from a multitude of receivers are selected by S1 8000 times a second and is converted to PCM digital form by the analog to digital convertor. It is then inserted into a time slot and is rate adapted to 1.554 Mbps for transmission on a T1 communications circuit. Each T1 time slot represents one communications channel. Figure 3.7 (b) shows how the T1 communications link is converted to the audio lines to the transceiver. PCM digital data contained in time slots from the T1 communications circuit are converted to analog voice signals by the digital to analog convertor. S2 routes the analog signal to the appropriate time transmitter section.

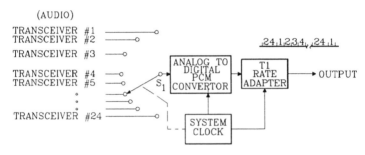

(A) BASE STATION TO COMMUNICATIONS LINK

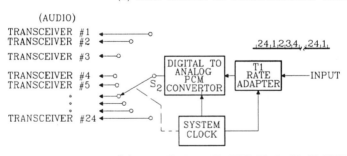

(B) COMMUNICATIONS LINK TO BASE STATION

Figure 3.7 Communications Link Processor Functional Block Diagram

3.2.3.7. Antenna Assembly

The antenna assembly transforms RF energy between the transceivers into electromagnetic waves propagating in free space. Antennas may be omni (equal energy in all directions) or directional (focused energy in a specific direction). Omni directional antennas may be first used to cover an entire cell direction). Omni directional antennas may be first used to cover an entire cell site area with one antenna. Directional antennas are used to divide cell site areas into several sectors, reducing co-channel interference and increasing the ability to reuse frequencies more often.

Base stations typically use two receive antennas to provide for diversity reception. Diversity reception allows the selection of one of multiple antennas that have a stronger received signal strength which minimizes the effects of Rayleigh fading. Antennas spaced 1/2 wavelength or more apart rarely correlate to a Rayleigh fade. While Mobile Station owners have been reluctant to place more than one cellular antenna on the car which has limited the use of diversity reception, diversity reception is almost always used in base stations.

3.2.3.8. Scanning Receiver

A scanning receiver is used to provide signal strength measurements for potential handoff channels. It is capable of tuning to any channel and measuring the received signal strength. The scanning receiver need only receive, although a standard Base Station transceiver may be used to allow one transceiver type to allow for the backup of voice, control, and scanning receiving equipment in the event of equipment failure [7].

3.2.3.9. Power Supplies

Primary power for cell sites is usually commercial AC power supplied by the local utility company. AC power is converted to regulated and filtered AC and DC voltage levels required by the equipment. In the event of a loss of primary power, backup supplies are provided to maintain operation. Backup energy sources may include batteries and a generator.

Energy sources supply equipment and cooling systems, therefore backup supplies should be capable of supplying higher than the average power demand. In 1989, a hurricane in Puerto Rico destroyed all land line communications. Due to good planning, cellular communications was unaffected and became the primary telecommunications service. The loading of the cooling systems increased with the excess demand which occurred in the disaster situation [8].

3.3. MOBILE TELEPHONE SWITCHING OFFICE

A MTSO coordinates all of the base stations within its network, routes signals to and from the PSTN, and provides administrative and maintenance functions. The MTSO has no required standards and its implementation is often proprietary. The mobile telephone switching office is similar to a land line switching center. An MTSO has the ability to switch the mobile to either the land line telephone network, another mobile, or private lines.

3.3.1. Mobile Telephone Switching Office Operation

The MTSO processes requests for service from mobile stations and landline callers. The MTSO performs call processing functions by decoding and creating call progress tones, receiving and translating dialed digits, and routing call paths. When an MTSO recognizes a request for service, it validates the request with stored information in its subscriber database. The MTSO receives dialed digits from the MS and translates the dialed digits to an appropriate dialing pattern for the PSTN (such as DTMF). When a call is received from a landline caller, the MTSO decodes the MS number and identifies to the switch where to connect the call. When a call path is to be completed (both parties to be connected) the MTSO controller identifies to the switch assembly which communication circuits must be connected.

3.3.2. Mobile Telephone Switching Office Detailed Description

Figure 3.8 shows an MTSO which consists of controllers, switching assembly, communication processors, operator terminal, subscriber database, and power supplies. The controllers are the brain of the entire cellular system as they guide the MTSO by creating and interpreting commands to and from the Base Stations and coordinating communications links to the PSTN. The switching assembly links voice connections from the Base Stations to the PSTN land lines. Communications processors convert the transmission medium which may be fiber, copper, or microwave links to signals that are processed by the switch assembly. Operator terminals allow the supervision and maintenance of the system. A subscriber database contains customer specified features and billing records. As with the Base Station, the MTSO has power supplies and backup energy sources to allow system operation to be maintained when a failure occurs.

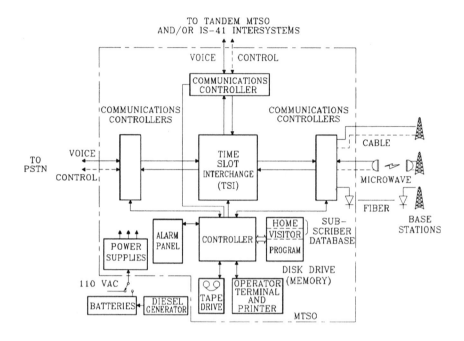

Figure 3.8 Mobile Telephone Switching Office Block Diagram

3.3.2.1. Controllers

Controllers provide for coordination of Base Stations, MTSO switching functions, and PSTN connections. A cell site controller creates and interprets commands to and from the base station. The call controller commands the MTSO switch, validates customer requests for access to the system, maintains billing records from both airtime and PSTN usage, and monitors for equipment failures. Communications controllers process and buffer voice and data information among the MTSO, Base Stations, and PSTN [9].

3.3.2.2. Switching Assembly

The switching assembly allows connections between Base Station communications channels and PSTN communications channels and is the heart of the MTSO. There are two types of switching connection systems in use: space division and time division. Space division switches complete a physical connection between associated lines. Time slot interchange (TSI) switching systems have evolved to allow a digital signal path to be formed between associated lines without a dedicated connection by temporary storage of time slot information. Almost all cellular switches are digital and have a much higher efficiency.

Figure 3.9 shows a simplified block diagram of a time slot interchange (TSI) system. The incoming and outgoing transmission links are in digital form where each transmission link is composed of time slots and frames. A time slot represents one communication channel and a time frame represents the maximum number of channels to be switched.

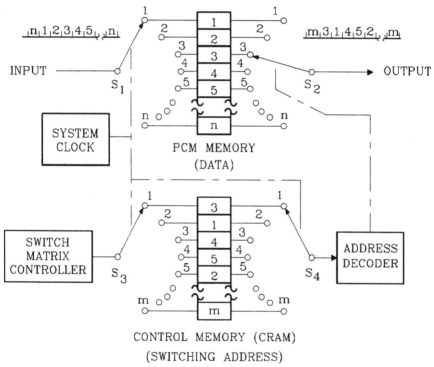

Figure 3.9 Time Slot Interchange (TSI) Simplified Block Diagram

Serial data is composed of slots and frames which are applied to S1 where the system clock coordinates S1 so each time slot is assigned a particular memory location in the PCM memory section. At the same time, the switch matrix controller calculates the number of the output time slot number to be associated with the PCM memory location. This number is stored in the Control Ram (CRAM) via S3. After the PCM memory and CRAM memories have been completely loaded, S4 is positioned to read the

CRAM memory from beginning to end which the address contents are decoded to position S2 to the correct PCM memory location. For a more detailed description of a TSI system see Motorola Corporation, "EMX Switch Functional Theory," 68P81052E49-0, Schaumburg, IL, 1983.

3.3.2.3. Communications Link Processors

The communications link processors provide interface between the communications channels and the MTSO switching assembly. Typically, the communications links are of T1 form, 24 64 kbps time division voice channels, which are grouped together by a group multiplexer [10]. The group multiplexer combines a multiple of T1 serial data links by compressing them into high speed signals for application to the Time Slot Interchange (TSI) switch assembly (see figure 3.10 (a)). The group demultiplexer separates the high speed TSI output by expanding them back into a multiple of T1 serial data links (see figure 3.10 (b)). In addition to the compression and expansion of data formats, the communications link processor must be capable of monitoring and inserting signaling commands from each of the channels.

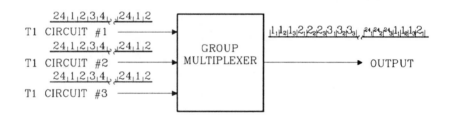

(A) CIRCUIT BANK TO TSI

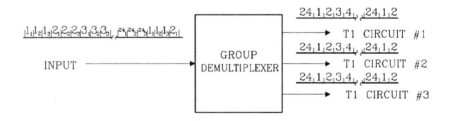

(B) TSI TO CIRCUIT BANK

Figure 3.10 Group Multiplexer Block Diagram

3.3.2.4. Operator Terminals

The man machine interface to the MTSO is accomplished through teletype or CRT display terminals. While MTSO operation is performed by controllers, maintenance and administrative functions are accomplished by data terminals which consist of a display device and keyboard. Maintenance operator terminals allow for software loading, diagnostics, and fault isolation. Administrative operator terminals allow the entry and extraction of subscriber database information.

3.3.2.5. System Media Storage

The MTSO system contains stored programs and databases and allows connection to external databases. Programs and databases are stored on magnetic disks and tape drives. Programs instruct the MTSO on system operations that are to be performed. Internal databases maintain home, visiting, and unauthorized subscriber information. External databases include an authentication center and other system interfaces. Internal databases imply ownership by the system operator and external databases relate to billing clearinghouse service providers. Databases need not be located together or at the switching center.

Stored Programs

Software programs are stored on magnetic disk to support call processing, cell site equipment control, maintenance, and office administration. Stored programs are uploaded and downloaded to and from the magnetic disk by the tape drive. Some systems allow the updating of cell site software by transfer via the data links [11].

Internal Database

The subscriber database maintains customer records based on a Mobile Identification Number (MIN) and Electronic Serial Number (ESN). Each customer has a user profile which includes selected long distance carrier, calling restrictions, service fee charge rates, and other network options. This database allows billing records to be maintained and can be divided into a Home Location Register (HLR), Visited Location Register (VLR), and Equipment Identity Register (EIR).

The HLR is a database of customers registered to the home cellular system. It contains semi-permanent subscriber information such as ESN, MIN, feature profile information, and current location information. The VLR is a database of the temporary customers not registered to the home cellular system. It contains temporary subscriber information such as ESN, MIN, and feature profile information. The EIR is a database which may contain equipment profile information. This is used as a validation list where equipment may be authoriazed or denied service based on if the unit has been stolen, or has poor performance characteristics.

External Databases

The Authentication Center (AC) is a database not typically part of the cellular system network. This is the clearinghouse where roamers may be validated and billing services provided. In the future, some of the services provided by the clearinghouses will be handled via intersystem links defined for the cellular network which allows direct access to the home database.

3.3.2.6. Power Supplies

As with the Base Station, primary power for the MTSO is usually commercial AC power supplied by the local utility company. AC power is converted to regulated and filtered AC and DC voltage levels required by the equipment. In the event of a loss of primary power, backup supplies are provided to maintain operation. Backup energy sources may include batteries and a generator.

3.4. COMMUNICATION LINKS

Communication links between the MTSO are analog or digital and use either copper, fiber optics, or radio transmission facilities. Communications links carry both data and voice information. Redundant data links are usually provided to prevent a single link failure from disabling communications.

Analog voice links transfer information by a voltage amplitude or frequency shift which changes in proportion to the original audio signal. Digital transmission transfer quantized binary information which represents the amplitude of the original audio signal. Almost all communications links today utilize Pulse Coded Modulation (PCM) digital transmission.

To allow the sharing of a communications channel between one or more users, subrate multiplexing may be used. Subrate multiplexing compresses data so that more than one user may share a communications channel. Figure 3.11 shows an accessory data compression device which allows up to 4 audio inputs to share one communications channel.

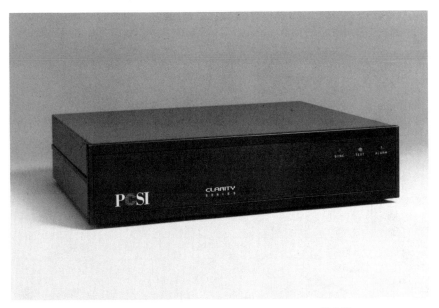

Figure 3.11 T1 Data Compression (photo courtesy of PCSI)

While signaling between the MTSO and base stations occurs on a communications circuit dedicated as a data link, communication between the MTSO and the PSTN and other cellular systems is usually accomplished by a separate X.25 or SS7 signaling network. X.25 typically has a slower signaling protocol and concerns exist regarding its capability to handle the large information transfer that will be necessary in the future. The primary advantages of SS7 as opposed to X.25 is the switching speed,[6] redundancy, global title translation, and the ability to use ISUP to support both intersystems and connections to the PSTN.

Delays in X.25 control signal routing would cause transients in handoffs and might not pass signaling data fast enough for real time roamer verification. Global title translation allows a single message identifier (the telephone number) to route the call through a plurality of Signal Transfer Points (STPs) to reach its final destination. This lets the network STPs find

---

6   Some X.25 implementations such as the AT&T Accu + net packet are as fast as SS7.

destinations where otherwise, each MTSO would have to contain system routing information for every mobile telephone number. The separation of control signaling and voice data allows for rapid control signal message transfer prior to the establishment of voice circuit. Figure 3.12 shows a sample SS7 signaling network.

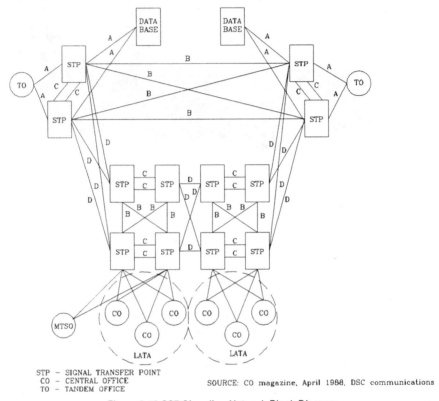

STP − SIGNAL TRANSFER POINT
CO − CENTRAL OFFICE
TO − TANDEM OFFICE

SOURCE: CO magazine, April 1988, DSC communications

Figure 3.12 SS7 Signaling Network Block Diagram

3.4.1. Landline

Landline communications links have large bandwidths and highly stable channel quality. Radio channels have limited bandwidths and channel quality varies rapidly. Similar to the evolution of radio transmission efficiency, landline transmission mediums were optimized to increase their efficiency. The utilization of transmission links was first exploited by frequency dividing the bandwidth of the communications link into several channels. The format and division of these links were defined as transmission carriers (e.g. N carrier, P carrier).

In 1962, the first digital transmission link was installed between Chicago and Skokie, Illinois [12]. The basis of this T carrier transmission format (figure 3.13) is the Time Division Multiplexing (TDM) of several digitized analog voice channels onto one communications circuit [13]. The T1 communications circuit is divided into time frames, frames contain 24 time slots plus a framing bit, and each slot contains eight bits of information. For voice transmission, each analog voice channel is sampled at 8000 times per second and converted to a PCM digital word. The 8000 samples x 8 bits per sample results in a data rate of 64 kbps and it is referred to as a DS0 (one channel). 24 DS0s plus a framing bit are time multiplexed onto the high speed T1 channel frame. Therefore, with a frame length of 193 bits, we have a data rate of 8000 x 193 = 1.544 Mbps.

Figure 3.13 DS1 Frame Structure

While a majority of leased communications links use a DS1 (also referred to as a T1 trunk) digital transmission format, the actual leased circuit may consist of a combination of copper wire, microwave, or fiber. Further technology advances have allowed several DS1 transmission links to be further compressed onto other high speed communications links (see table 3.2).

Table 3.2 Digital Transmission

(source: Dr. George Calhoun, Digital Cellular Radio, (MA: Artech House, 1988), p. 181.)

Number of Voice Circuits	Digital Signal Number	System Input	Bit Rate (Mbps)
24	DS-1	24 Analog	1.544
48	DS-1C	2 DS-1	3.152
96	DS-2	4 DS-1	6.312
672	DS-3	28 DS-1	44.736
4032	DS-4	6 DS-3	274.176

3.4.2. Radio Communications Links

Radio transmission facilities may be installed by the cellular system operator to overcome the burden of leasing communications links. Microwave communications circuits require a direct line of sight and are affected by weather, particularly rain. With few exceptions, an FCC license is required to install microwave equipment and in densely populated areas, obtaining a license may be a problem. While other radio links can be used such as 800 MHz radio, due to bandwidth efficiency and lack of available spectrum, almost all radio links involve microwave transmission and use the same T1 and other data rates as the landline communications channels.

3.4.3. Fiberoptic

Fiberoptic transmission links have enormous transmission bandwidth capacity. Unfortunately, gaining the right of way to install fiber cable between transmission points is costly and leasing fiber transmission links from the local phone company is also extremely expensive. Although challenges in obtaining fiber facilities have limited the use of fiber in cellular systems, fiber links may reduce equipment costs in the future. Fiber links can carry a modulated carrier at a much higher frequency which can be frequency translated at the cell site [14]. This allows moving base station controllers and RF equipment to a central location and reduces the cell site equipment size, complexity, and cost.

3.5. PSTN INTERCONNECTION

The MTSO is the gateway from the cellular system to the land line (PSTN) telephone network. The combination of the MTSO and the PSTN provides the ability to switch a cellular system Mobile Station to any land line telephone. Cellular PSTN connections are classified as Type 1, Type 2A, or Type 2B. Type 1 facilities are similar to a PBX connection. No ANI (Automatic Number Identification) information is available to the MTSO from the PSTN. For a type 1 connection, a cellular system operator must rely on the LEC (Local Exchange Carrier) for inter-LATA service (long distance). Type 2A facilities can access IXC (Inter Exchange Carriers) directly as the ANI is available. Type 2B facilities are used to connect the cellular carrier to a high-usage end office to allow direct connection to customers in the end office area [15].

More than one PSTN interconnection point should be used to provide for redundancy. In the 1989 San Francisco earthquake, only one PSTN interconnection was provided to a central office which almost collapsed [16]. Had the central office been destroyed, alternate PSTN interconnection routing would have been a major problem.

3.6. NETWORK OPERATION

The cellular system is composed of network elements which form an integrated radio communications system. The cellular system allows landline users to call Mobile Stations, Mobile Stations to call landline users, Mobile Stations to call other Mobile Stations, and calls to be maintained as a Mobile Station moves from one cell site area to another.

3.6.1. Land to Mobile Call

A landline user calls a Mobile Station (see figure 3.14) by dialing the MS telephone number. The call is routed through the PSTN to the MTSO. The MTSO then commands all the Base Stations in its system to page the MS[7]. If the MS is active in the system, it responds to the page by locking onto the strongest control channel and attempting access and indicating the access is a result of a page message. Authorized access is verified by comparing the received MS MIN/ESN to stored MIN/ESNs in the MTSO subscriber

---

7   It is possible to page only in areas where the MS is known to be to minimize the required number of paging messages that are sent by each cell site.

database. The Base Station then assigns the MS to a voice channel. The MS tunes to the assigned voice channel and begins to transpond a SAT (see 2.3.2.1) with the MS. After the BS has received the correct SAT on the voice channel, the BS sends a message to the MS to alert (ring) the user that an incoming call is to be received. When the MS alerts the operator, the MS returns the 10 kHz ST (see 2.3.2.2). This alert acknowledgment is relayed back to the PSTN to allow the landline party to hear a ringing signal. When the operator answers the ringing signal (usually by pressing SND), the MS stops sending the ST. This confirms to the MTSO that the user has answered the call. The call is then connected and conversation begins.

If the landline party hangs up, a command is sent from the MTSO to the MS to disconnect. If the MS goes on-hook (by pressing the END key), the MS transmits ST for 1.8 seconds and terminates transmission.

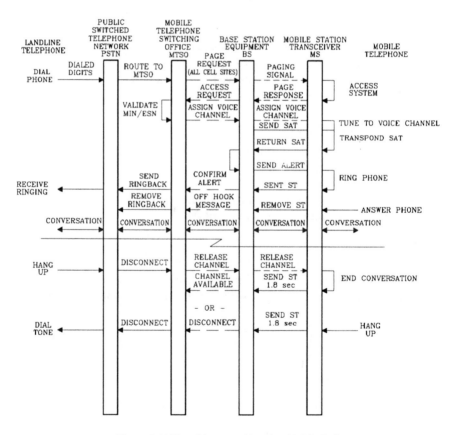

Figure 3.14 Flow Diagram of Land to Mobile Call

3.6.2. Mobile to Land Call

A Mobile Station calls a landline party (see figure 3.15) by dialing the landline telephone number and pressing the SEND key. The MS then scans and locks onto the strongest control channel and attempts access by sending the dialed digits and indicating the access is a result of an origination request (see 2.4.3). Authorized access is verified by comparing the received MS MIN/ESN to stored MIN/ESNs in the MTSO subscriber database. If access is successful (verified valid MIN/ESN in the MTSO database), the Base Station assigns the MS to an analog voice channel. When the MS has tuned to the assigned voice channel, it begins to transpond a SAT with the MS. Upon receiving SAT from the MS, the MTSO dials the received digits to the PSTN where the call is then connected to reach the landline party. The mobile operator receives the call progress tones (ring or busy) from the dialed destination. When the landline party answers, conversation begins.

If the landline party hangs up, a command is sent from the MTSO to the MS to disconnect. If the MS goes on-hook (by pressing the END key), the MS transmits ST for 1.8 seconds and terminates transmission.

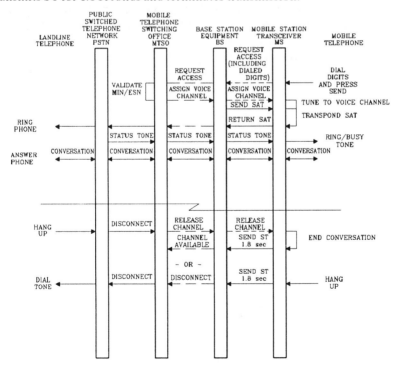

Figure 3.15 Mobile to Land Flow Diagram

3.6.3. Mobile to Mobile Call

The process for completing MS to MS calls is similar to those described for MS calls to and from landline users except the calls between the mobile units that are served by the same MTSO do not need to be routed through the PSTN.[8]

3.6.4. Handoff

As an MS moves out of its serving cell site area while a call is in progress, its received signal level and/or the Signal to Noise Ratio (SNR) decreases. For system areas with co-channel interference, the SNR will decrease and for systems that do not have a co-channel interference, the received signal strength will decrease. The measured signal quality levels at the base station are averaged over approximately 100 msec because they fluctuate due to multipath fading [17]. When the SNR, RSSI or a combination of both falls below a predetermined level, adjacent Base Station equipment is instructed to measure the signal strength of the MS (see figure 3.16). The Base Station with the highest signal quality is selected as the handoff cell site. The selected BS begins to transmit on a new channel and the MS is commanded from the serving cell site to tune to the new voice channel. The MTSO then switches the communications circuit to the new serving Base Station and conversation continues.

---

8   Typically, cell sites are connected via dedicated lines leased from the PSTN.

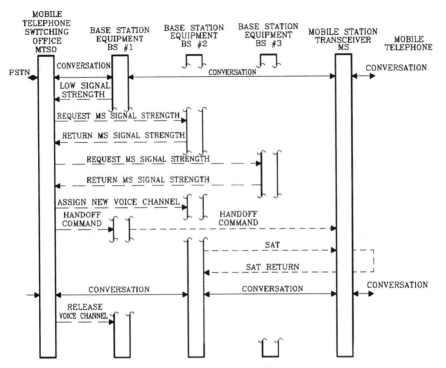

Figure 3.16 Handoff Flow Diagram

3.6.5. Roamer Call Handling

When visiting customers attempt to use a cellular system, call processing may deviate significantly. Two types of visitors may exist: registered and unregistered roamers. Due to the extensive cellular fraud, roaming may not be automatic.

When a visiting customer attempts to access the system for the first time, the call may be redirected to a system operator. This operator may ask for registration information such as how long the customer may be in the area and telephone or charge card numbers to secure revenues. The operator may then allow the visiting customer to become a temporary registered roamer and operate free from restricted calling. A visiting roamer may receive calls by having the calling party call a system access number and then dialing the complete roamer's telephone number.

3.7. DESIGN PROCESS FOR A CELLULAR NETWORK

Designing a cellular system is a long and tedious task that continuously changes. A cellular system is composed of radio coverage cell areas created by RF transmission from interconnected Base Stations. The selection of frequencies and power levels at each Base Station determines the cell size and system serving capacity limits. Power level is influenced by antenna directivity, gain, type, and surrounding terrain conditions.

Cellular system design is affected by radio propagation factors, strategic planning, and system expansion requirements. Radio propagation characteristics affect how efficient the system can be designed. Every cellular system is unique so strategic planning requirements include data acquisition, MTSO and cell site location selection, equipment procurement, and validation. System capacity expansion involves optimizing the existing system and adding/dividing radio service coverage areas.

3.7.1. Radio Propagation

The U.S. cellular system operates in the 800 MHz region which has unique attenuation, fading characteristics, and signal quality requirements. Attenuation varies as a function of distance and terrain. Fading characteristics result in a variance of received signal level in short distance intervals. Signal quality is limited by both received level and interfering signal strength.

3.7.1.1. Attenuation

As RF energy is radiated into free space, its power is distributed over a 20 dB/decade.[9] This means, as the distance increases from the source by a factor of 10, the power is reduced by a factor of 100. As RF energy propagates over various terrains, the attenuation is approximately 40 dB per decade [18], which is due to signal scattering and absorption. In heavy foliage areas, attenuation in excess of 60 dB per decade may be observed. Changes in seasons result in the reduction of attenuation which results in movement of cell site boundaries.

---

9   If energy is focused into a narrow beam, attenuation in free space can be less than 20 dB/dec.

3.7.1.2. Fading Characteristics

Signal fading is a result of multipath propagation where the same signal is received at different times. The combination of these signals in and out of phase results in variations of signal strength points at short distances. Multipath fading occurs in areas where a direct path is received from the cell site tower and a signal reflected from a building or hillside within several hundred feet. The statistical variation of these fluctuations is termed Rayleigh fading. Figure 3.17 shows a simplified Rayleigh fading variation where the fades occur approximately every 1/2 wavelength, approximately 7 inches apart [19].

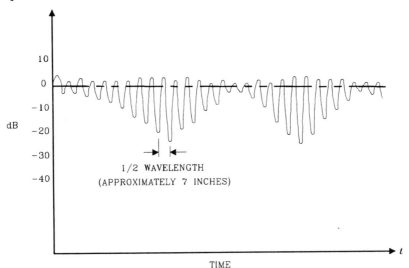

Figure 3.17 Rayleigh Fading Characteristics

3.7.1.3. Signal Quality

Signal quality varies throughout a cellular system area and may be degraded by Carrier to Noise (C/N) or Carrier to Interference (C/I). In a Carrier to Noise environment, communications quality degrades as the Mobile Station moves into a low signal strength area which is limited by thermal noise. For a Carrier to Interference environment, communications quality degrades as the MS moves into an area which has an interfering signal. In a single cell system where the mobile station can wander out of cellular service completely, the limiting factor is how much signal is available to overcome the background noise (C/N ratio). In mature cellular systems, as most in the U.S. are rapidly becoming, the limiting factor is how much signal is available to overcome the interference from other cell sites (C/I ratio).

The advantage of a cellular system is its ability to reuse frequencies when the attenuation from one transmitting source will interfere little with another. The minimum distance that is allowable is determined by the maximum desired carrier to interference ratio (C/I).

formula $D/R = (3N)^{1/2}$ or $N = (D/R)^2/3$ [20]

Once the D/R (distance to reuse) is calculated, cell sites frequencies can be selected not to interfere with other cell sites.

3.7.2. Strategic Planning

A strategic plan includes collecting system area information, establishing the type of service area, targeting key locations, cell site and MTSO location selection, conforming to government regulations, equipment purchasing, construction, and verification testing.

Physical and demographic information are gathered first. Using maps, transportation thoroughfares, industrial parks, shipping ports, railway centers, and airports are identified as possible high usage areas. Targeting coverage areas for major roadway corridors is performed by studying traffic patterns. Using the terrain and marketing demographic data, the cellular system area is divided into RF coverage areas. This targets a gross area where cell site towers can be located. For the U.S. market, government regulations include quality of service and time interval for service offering [21]. Equipment manufacturers and their systems are reviewed so purchase contracts and financing plans may be initiated. Construction schedules are developed and labor contracts are signed. During various stages of equipment installation, verification testing is performed to ensure all of the planning goals are being realized.

Designing a cellular system is not an exact science. The many available options and requirements result in trade offs between each of the design criteria. Cell Sites have a maximum serving capacity that is dependent on manufacturer's equipment specifications and the system implementation. This results in different manufacturers' base station equipment having the same RF coverage area being capable of serving a different number of subscribers. System usage will vary with traffic patterns, making the maximum required capacity much higher than the average usage requires. The inability to obtain exact cell site locations results in trade offs between ideal system design and an economically achievable system.

3.7.2.1. Data Acquisition

All cellular systems are unique as the terrain and system usage varies between systems. Raw data to be accumulated includes system specifications, road maps, population density distribution maps, significant urban centers locations, marketing demographic data, elevation data, PSTN switch center locations, and airport locations.

System specifications are contained in EIA-553 and IS-20B. Terrain maps are usually entered into a computer for simulations therefore maps should have longitude and latitude identification. Population density distribution maps obtained by the census bureau of the Library of Congress, are used with marketing demographic data to project the service requirements by service areas. For established markets with similar demographic data, the demand for and usage amounts of cellular service can be equated with the population density distribution to determine the forecasted demand. Elevation data may be accumulated from existing data or may be created in a variety of ways. The USGS provides elevation data on magnetic media that can be input to computer simulation programs directly [22]. A new method of acquiring elevation and terrain data is photogrammetry. Photogrammetry is a process through which terrain elevation data can be accumulated from using a stereo image or photographs in 3-D. PSTN switch center locations are prime targets for MTSO locations. This minimizes trunking length requirements between the cellular system and the PSTN. Airport locations are required to ensure towers are not constructed that will interfere with air safety. All of this information is used by the engineering staff to project the minimum equipment requirements to meet this service demand.

3.7.2.2. System Simulation

Once potential Cell Site locations are selected, RF simulations begin (see figure 3.18). Elevation and terrain data is input to an RF simulation program to show the relative coverage area. After simulations are completed, temporary towers are usually installed to verify received levels in the field prior to final construction.

System simulation predicts the quality of service which includes signal strength levels, acceptable interference levels, and blockage. When individual cell site simulation is completed, system simulations are performed. These include adjacent and alternate cells' propagation levels to verify acceptable carrier to interference and carrier to noise ratios.

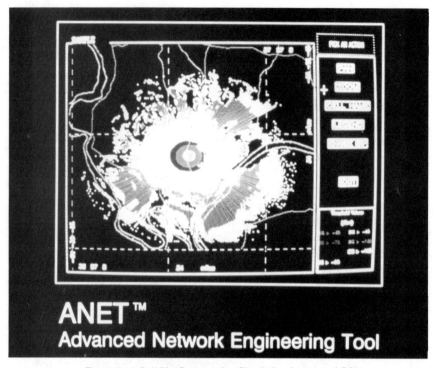

Figure 3.18 Cell Site Propagation Simulation (courtesy LCC)

3.7.2.3. Cell Site Location Selection

After optimal cell site possibilities have been simulated and tests sites verified, site acquisition, licenses and construction permits begin. Because optimal cell sites often cannot be obtained, alternate locations are considered. If a particular selected cell site location cannot be obtained, a tolerance of +/- 1/4 radius is acceptable for cell site location [23]. Cell site locations can be evaluated for the possibility of a microwave link between the MTSO or to another tower to be relayed to the MTSO (referred to as a hop). When a cell site selection has been proposed, it may be possible to use an existing T.V. or radio tower. Use of such towers must be approached with caution as microwave links focus energy into a narrow beam and towers that can flex may result in varying microwave reception. Access to roads and utilities must be considered. Locations such as a top of a mountain may be ideal for radio propagation. However, maintenance access and power routing requirements become challenging. A final consideration to proposed cell site locations is the anticipation of growth patterns. There is no need to construct a 500 foot tower if within a short period of time the cell site area will have to be divided.

3.7.2.4. MTSO Location Selection

A mobile telephone switching office contains a substantial amount of equipment and is usually staffed by technicians and administrators. The MTSO requires accessibility and utilities such as electricity, water, and sewage. The location should allow cost effective access (close proximity to high rate data such as a fiber link) to PSTN interconnections near a digital central office [24]. To allow for alternate routing in disaster situations, the MTSO should be linked to the PSTN via more than one central office [25]. A clear path for microwave links should be considered to link to base station equipment reducing the need for leased landline connections.

3.7.2.5. Equipment Selection

While cost may be a major contributing factor for the selection of a system supplier, service support, features availability, redundancy, and system expansibility are also deciding factors. For the smaller cellular system operator without a qualified engineering staff, service support is critical. System features such as call forwarding or call waiting, add additional billing revenues in addition to a competitive advantage. Redundancy maintains system operation after equipment fails. As a cellular system expands, the equipment selected should have a cost effective expansibility.

Service Support

System support can vary from the supply of hardware with no assistance to turn key operations where the equipment manufacturer performs the system layout, construction, and starts up operation. While larger system operators have skilled staff who can perform engineering and technical support functions, smaller operators must turn to the manufacturer or outside consultants to plan and construct the cellular system.

Features

Equipment features include software and hardware options that increase reliability, efficiency, or add to a list of billable services. Hardware features include intersystem interfacing such as IS-41 [26], equipment redundancy, SS7 signaling controllers, and voice mailbox. Software features include call forwarding, call waiting, three way calling, and multiple ESNs with the same phone number.

Redundancy

Redundancy allows a system to keep operating despite equipment failures. Redundancy increases equipment requirements, therefore the increased cost of spare equipment must be justified by the potential lost airtime revenues during equipment outages. There are two types of redundancy, 2N or N + 1. 2N redundancy requires every equipment to have its own individual backup unit. N + 1 redundancy only requires one spare to be used for any one of the N units that fails.

Expansibility

Cost effective expansion is one of the original Bell System goals [27]. Cellular equipment is often rated by its maximum system serving capacity. Once this capacity limit has been exceeded, the system must be expanded if possible or replaced. Capacity may be increased by sectoring existing cell site areas or constructing additional cell sites. Some system equipments are easier to upgrade (such as sectoring) than others.

3.7.2.6. Construction

When the cell site locations have been acquired, permits and licenses must be obtained from state, county, city, PUC (Public Utilities Commission), and other regulatory agencies. Construction must begin to meet time deadlines, equipment must be purchased, and safety procedures must be followed.

Obtaining construction permits may be challenging as neighborhoods rarely want an ugly radio tower in their area. This has become such an issue that one method of installing a radio tower was to disguise it as a church bell tower [28]. Environmental considerations such as wind and earthquakes must be taken into consideration and will affect the cell site design and cost.

The FCC must give site approval and license the use of microwave if used. The Federal Aviation Administration (FAA) controls the height, marking, and lighting of towers. Any tower over 200 feet and smaller towers within a 5 mile radius (approximate) from an airport must be approved by the FAA [29].

Time deadlines depicted by a business plan must be flexible. The business plan indicates a cost objective approach to establishing service and is established around regulations. Regulations include dates for service to be established to meet minimum quality requirements. Often, delays in site acquisition require continual adjustment to the business plan to meet regulation and service quality objectives. The U.S. Federal Communications

Commission (FCC) requires cellular service must cover over 75 percent of the service area [30]. The quality of service provided must meet minimum blockage and signal quality levels.

Equipment costs include a cell site building, tower, and radio equipment. Each cell site costs between $400,000 (rural areas) to $1,750,000 (urban areas) for the building, tower, and all electronics equipment [31] [32]. Considerations for the cell site construction includes cost, deployment time, deployment flexibility, portability, and sturdiness [33].

3.7.2.7. System Verification

System verification includes the determination of RF coverage quality and system operation. Signal quality is tested for individual cells first, then adjacent cells are measured to determine system performance. System operation is verified by measuring the signal quality level at handoff, blockage performance, and the number of dropped calls.

RF coverage area verification ensures that a minimum coverage area percentage has been satisfied. The received signal strength and interference levels are measured to locate holes where the signal level falls below an acceptable level due to terrain and obstructions. These areas may require another cell site or may be filled in with repeaters that amplify the existing signal and focus the energy into a dead spot (i.e. a parking garage).

System operation can be verified by recording the signal levels received by a test mobile station when handoff and access occurs. Blocking probability can be calculated from the number of access attempts rejected by the system. The test equipment shown in figure 3.19 monitors and records the signal quality levels as the test mobile station moves throughout the system area. This resultant data can then be plotted to determine where signal levels and handoff thresholds need to be increased and decreased.

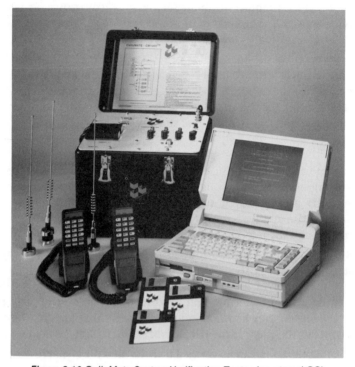

Figure 3.19 CelluMate System Verification Tester (courtesy LCC)

3.7.3. System Expansion

Systems may be fine tuned to increase the serving capacity and quality of service. System capacity may be increased by adding directional antennas, using underlay and overlay rings, frequency planning, and cell site division. Signal quality may be increased by adjusting power level, antenna heights, and adding repeaters.

Capacity expansion is made possible by the ability to reuse frequencies in a cellular system more often. Increasing signal quality is a result of targeting the coverage area and level of wanted signal. Directional antennas, underlay and overlay rings, and cell site division all reduce co-channel interference to other cell site areas. After co-channel interference has been reduced, frequency planning may assign an additional number of repeated frequencies therefore increasing system serving capacity. Directional antennas are used to divide cell site areas into sectors. Underlay and overlay rings lower the output power of some of the channels within a cell site area. As a Mobile Station moves toward the center of the cell, a handoff occurs to the lower power channels. Cell site division is a result of adding new transmitting locations within a cell site area with a reduced power level for each of them.

Signal quality may be improved by increasing the desired signal level within the cell site area. By adjusting radiated power and antenna heights, the boundaries of a cell site area may be increased or reduced. The use of repeaters allows a cell site boundary area to be extended or dead spots to be filled in within a cell site area. Repeaters offer a low cost and low complexity solution to increasing the coverage area. Figure 3.20 shows a picture of a repeater station.

Figure 3.20 Cellular Repeater Station (courtesy Antenna Specialists)

3.8. SUMMARY

A cellular system is an integration of radio and network technology. It consists of Base Stations (BS), a Mobile Telephone Switching Office (MTSO), communication links, and PSTN interconnections.

Base stations convert RF signals to and from mobile stations for transfer to and from the MTSO. Each base station performs call processing, maintenance, and diagnostic functions. Base stations consist of a control section, transceivers, RF amplifiers, receiver multicouplers, RF combiner, communications processors, scanning receiver, power supplies, and an antenna assembly.

An MTSO coordinates the base stations within its network and routes signals to and from the PSTN. The MTSO also provides administrative, maintenance, and diagnostic functions. The MTSO consists of controllers, switching assembly, communications processors, operator terminal, subscriber database, and backup energy sources.

Communications links between the network elements use either copper, fiber optics, or radio transmission facilities. Communications links are typically digital and have several channels time multiplexed on one data link. Signaling between network elements is either by dedicated links or via the PSTN by using a X.25 or SS7 packet system. X.25 is typically slower than SS7 and does not have global title translation capability.

The gateway from the MTSO to the PSTN is accomplished by either a level 1, level 2 or level 2A interface. A level 1 interface appears as an end telephone which does not allow the obtaining of all signaling control messages. The level 2 appears as a PBX system. A level 2A appears as a central office where all control signals and trunking can be accomplished. More than one PSTN interconnection should be used to provide redundancy.

Designing a cellular system is a tedious task that continuously changes. The selection of frequencies and power levels at each base station determines the system capacity limits. Radio channel quality is affected by attenuation, signal fading, and interfering signals. Planning and completing a cellular system requires data acquisition, system simulation, cell site and MTSO location selection, equipment selection, construction, and verification. As a system matures, capacity may be increased by adding directional antennas, using underlay and overlay rings, frequency planning, and cell site division.

References:

[1] CTIA Winter Exposition, Donald Cox, *"PCN: What is it and Where is it Going,"* Reno, Nevada, (February 6, 1990).

[2] Electronic Industries Association, EIA-553, *"Mobile Station - Land Station Compatibility Specification,"* (1990).

[3] Electronic Industries Association, EIA Interim Standard IS-20-A, Recommended Minimum Standards for 800 MHz Cellular Land Stations, (February 1986).

[4] Hug, Saiful, Design Engineer, LCC, Arlington, VA. Interview, July 1991.

[5] American Telephone and Telegraph Company, *The Bell System Technical Journal,* (Murray Hill, New Jersey). January 1979, Vol. 58, No. 1.

[6] Astronet, *"Astronet Practices,"* Section 30-000-02, Issue 2, (August 1987), pp. 38-39.

[7] *Ibid.*, p. 62.

[8] CTIA Winter Exposition, *"Disaster Experiences,"* Reno, Nevada, (February 6, 1990).

[9] U.S. Patent 4,887,265, Packet-Switched Cellular Telephone System, Kenneth Felix, (December, 1989).

[10] Motorola Corporation, 68P81052E27-0, *"EMX Switch Description,"* Schaumburg, IL, (1983), pp. 1-2.

[11] *"Astronet Practices,"* p. 56.

[12] Dr. George Calhoun, *Digital Cellular Radio*, (MA: Artech House, 1988), p.147.

[13] William Stallings, *Data and Computer Communications*, (New York: Macmillan Publishing Company, 2nd ed., 1988).

[14] T.S. Chu and M.J. Gans, *"Fiber Optic Micro Cellular Radio,"* IEEE 1991 Vehicular Technology Conference, pp. 339-344.

[15] Zweifach, Steve. "Cellular and the Public Switched Network." *CTIA Industry Report*, Volume 7, No. 7, (July 1991), pp. 29-30.

[16] CTIA Winter Exposition, *"Disaster Experiences,"* Reno, Nevada, (February 6, 1990).

[17] *"Astronet Practices,"* pp. 19-20.

[18] Lee, William, *Mobile Cellular Telecommunications Systems,* (McGraw Hill, 1989), pp. 104-105.

[19] *The Bell System Technical Journal,* pp. 98-99.

[20] Astronet, *"Frequency Reuse in Cellular Systems, Engineering Consideration,"* (October 1986).

[21] FCC Regulations, Part 22, Subpart K, "Domestic Public Cellular Radio Telecommunications Service," 22.903, (June 1981).

[22] Hug, Saiful, Design Engineer, LCC, Arlington, VA. Interview, July 1991.

[23] *The Bell System Technical Journal,* p. 27.

[24] Chin, Bill, Cellular Network Consultant, Modern Office Systems Technology, Clifton, New Jersey. Interview, October 1990.

[25] CTIA Winter Exposition, *"Disaster Experiences,"* Reno, Nevada, (February 6, 1990).

[26] Electronic Industries Association, EIA Interim Standard IS-41-A, Cellular Systems Operation, February 1990.

[27] *The Bell System Technical Journal,* pp. 16-19.

[28] CTIA Winter Exposition, *"Right Place, Right Time: Cellular in the 90's,"* San Diego, Bob Tonsfeldt (Jan. 1991).

[29] CTIA Winter Exposition, *"Safety all the Time,"* San Diego, California, (February 17, 1991).

[30] FCC Regulations, Part 22, Subpart K, *"Domestic Public Cellular Radio Telecommunications Service,"* 22.903, June 1981.

[31] Chin. Interview, February 1991.

[32] Gaddy, Aubrey, Cellular Systems Designer, McCaw Cellular, Seattle, Washington. Interview, May 1991.

[33] James Proffitt and Joseph Cylwik, *"Rapid Deployment Custom Cell Sites,"* (IEEE 1990 Vehicular Technology Conference), pp. 183-190.

Chapter 4

Dual Mode Cellular

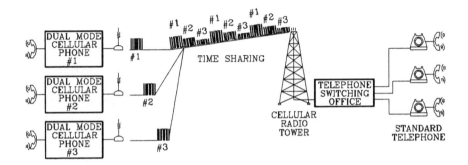

Figure 4.1 TDMA Digital Cellular

4.1. DUAL MODE CELLULAR INTRODUCTION

In 1988, the CTIA (Cellular Telecommunications Industry Association) created a UPR (User Performance Requirements) document which described a new generation of cellular equipment that could meet the growing needs of the cellular industry. The UPR did not specify analog or digital technology, it only designated system capacity requirements and the need for new features [1]. This chapter provides a high level overview of the operation of Dual Mode cellular equipment that conforms to IS-54 [2]. Descriptions in this chapter are used with reference to chapter 1 to cover the Analog cellular part of the Dual Mode equipment. Included in this chapter are semi-technical descriptions and functional block diagrams. For the experienced cellular engineer, this will be a basic systems introduction to Digital Cellular technology.

Dual Mode cellular technology uses digital transmission channels and has evolved from the existing Analog structure. While the digital transmission channels are physically different than their analog predecessor, the functional operation is similar. A Dual Mode transceiver consists of an analog and digital transceiver unit in one box. Digital transmission is preferred, so when a cellular system has digital capability, the Mobile Station will be assigned a digital channel first. If no digital channels are available, the Cellular System will assign an analog channel.

4.2. SYSTEM ATTRIBUTES

The Dual Mode digital cellular system meets the CTIA UPR goals by maintaining the same RF channel control channel technology, increasing the quality of voice transmission, providing cost effective capacity expansion, and maintaining a coordinated system control. The Dual Mode system maintains compatibility with the established access technology by allowing analog (EIA-553) and dual mode (IS-54) mobile stations to utilize the same analog control channels. Some of the voice channels are converted to allow digital transmission for multiplexing of several users on one RF channel. Even in varying radio conditions, the voice quality remains stable. Cost effective capacity expansion is accomplished by the time sharing of the digital RF channels, the ability to frequently reuse frequencies, the reduction of the minimum cell size, and the use of a low bit rate speech codec which performs data compression. A Mobile Switching Center (MSC) continues to provide the central control by transferring calls from one cell to another as the Mobile Station moves throughout the system.

4.2.1. Access Technology

A key requirement of the Dual Mode technology was compatibility with the existing EIA-553 cellular system while providing system capacity expansion and enhanced services [3]. This resulted in the use of the existing control channels for assignments to both analog and digital voice channels. The control channel structure was altered to include a digital capability indicator that is sent in the overhead messages and the inclusion of a new traffic channel assignment message that includes extra parameters for digital channel assignment.

4.2.2. Digital Transmission Quality

When a signal passes through a transmission medium, distortion and noise are added. A digital signal can be processed to enhance its resistance to distortion by signal regeneration, error detection, and error correction. Signal regeneration overcomes the addition of distortion and noise. When a signal is transmitted throughout a system, it creates a new signal without noise from a signal with noise (see figure 4.2) [4]. Error detection is used to determine if channel impairments have exceeded the tolerance to distortion. Error correction is the ability to correct for errors by providing redundant data to be used to correct error detected bits. All three of these digital features are used in the IS-54 system providing for a robust transmission channel. Figure 4.2 shows how noise is added to a digital signal, 4.2 (a) + 4.2 (b). By using ON/OFF threshold detection/conversion shown in figure 4.2 (c), the original signal can be regenerated (4.2 (d)).

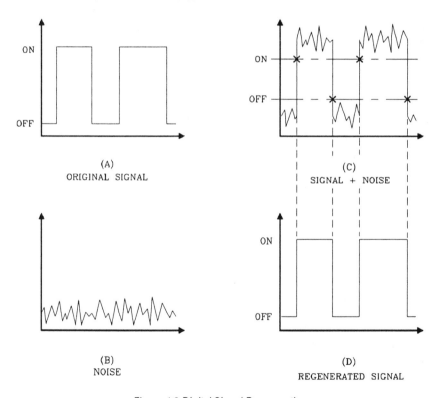

Figure 4.2 Digital Signal Regeneration

4.2.3. Capacity Expansion

The original technique of cell splitting to increase capacity has been enhanced by allowing time multiplexing users on the same RF channel, increasing the ability to reuse frequencies at closer distances, reducing the minimum cell size, and data compressing voice information by a speech codec. The combination of all of these factors supported in IS-54 allow cost effective capacity expansion.

4.2.3.1. Time Division Multiplexing

The dual mode system allows the time multiplexing of RF channels to allow several users to share the same RF channel. As shown in figure 4.1, Mobile Stations share the same RF channel by compressing voice information into short bursts and sharing with other users. Mobile Stations are synchronized by the Base Station so each Mobile Station only transmits in its particular time slot. Once received by the Base Station, the time shared signals are reconstructed (expanded) to individual voice channels and may be sent to the PSTN for land line routing.

4.2.3.2. Frequency Reuse

In analog FM cellular systems, increased capacity results from the ability to reuse the same RF channels. Frequency reuse is a function of the tolerance to co-channel interference [5]. It has been demonstrated that the phase shifted modulation used for digital channels is less susceptible to co-channel interference [6]. This allows the IS-54 DQPSK modulated transceiver channels to be reused more often within a system.

not true

4.2.3.3. Minimum Cell Size

The primary advantage of a cellular system remains in its ability to increase the serving capacity by dividing cell site coverage areas through power reduction and frequency reuse. The original EIA-553 specification allowed the reduction of Mobile Station power to a minimum of - 22 dBW (7 mW). This results in a minimum cell size of approximately 1/2 mile radius. A real capacity gain occurs with the ability to further divide cell site coverage areas [7]. The IS-54 standard created a new class of transceiver. This has a minimum power capability of - 34 dBW (400 uW), allowing a significant reduction in minimum cell size.

4.2.3.4. Speech Codec

The landline telephone network employs the use of 64 kbps companded PCM for the digital transmission of speech signals. Transmission of this 64 kbps digital signal on a land mobile radio channel would require a channel bandwidth wider than the current cellular channel bandwidths, thereby reducing spectral efficiency. To increase the transmission efficiency for the digital cellular system, the data rate must be reduced. This is accomplished with the use of a digital speech codec which removes redundancy in the waveform of the speech signal. The speech codec models the speech signal as the output of a vocal tract filter whose input is an appropriate excitation signal. The vocal tract filter's frequency response is specified by 8-10 parameters. The excitation signal can be digitally encoded at a data rate much lower than the original speech signal. The vocal tract and excitation information must be updated and retransmitted to characterize the changing speech signal. This update rate is usually once every 20 msec. The digital speech codec reduces the 64 kbps data input to 7950 bps.

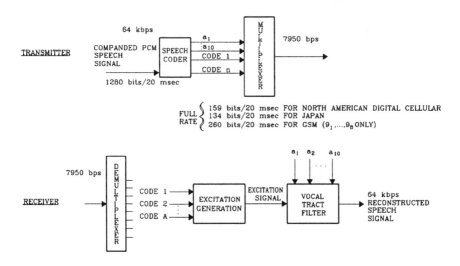

Figure 4.3 Speech Codec Simplified Block Diagram

4.2.4. System Control

A cellular system maintains voice transmission when a Mobile Station is moving from one cell to another cell by automatically switching the mobile station voice path from cell site to cell site. The Mobile Switching Center (MSC) coordinates the handoff from cell to cell and connects calls between the Mobile Station and PSTN. The dual mode MSC continues to create and interpret the necessary command signals to control the Mobile Stations via cell sites although increased handoff quality and distributed call processing are possible by a new system feature.

Mobile Assisted Handoff (MAHO) has been added to increase handoff voice quality and reduce call processing requirements. MAHO allows a serving base station to request potential handoff cell site signal strength measurements directly from the Mobile Station. This reduces the intrasystem signaling requirements and will reduce overall network complexity requirements.

While the Dual Mode cellular system can operate with only the existing control channels, 313 through 354, to allow rapid deployment of this technology, a method of implementation was developed that allowed the addition of a secondary set of control channels, 696 through 737. These are optional control channels and they permit an overlay type implementation of cell site equipment (see chapter 6).

4.3. SYSTEM PARAMETERS

Unlike early development of the cellular system in the 1970s, many choices of technology were available to meet the CTIA UPR requirements. Available options included SSB AM, Narrowband FM, and Time Division Multiple Access (TDMA) digital transmission. TDMA technology was accepted by the industry participants in early 1989. The selection of the TDMA technology was followed by the specification of frequency allocations, modulation type, digital signal processing, and RF channel structure.

4.3.1. Frequency Allocation

The existing spectral bandwidth allocation for public cellular services, 824-849 MHz and 869-894 MHz, was not increased and the 30 kHz channel bandwidth defined by EIA-553 was not changed. The two primary changes that occurred were the specification for converting individual analog FM voice channels into Π/4 Differential Quadrature Phase Shift Keying

(DQPSK) modulated time division digital channels and an ability to optionally convert a group of analog voice channels to additional control channels.

Each radio channel can become more spectral efficient by using TDMA digital technology. To allow gradual conversion of radio channels from analog to digital, the same 30 kHz channel bandwidth was maintained [8]. This permits channels to be converted individually as the demand for digital cellular increases.

4.3.2. Duplex Channels

The 50 MHz frequency allocation is divided into two 25 MHz blocks separated by 45 MHz. The same 45 MHz forward and reverse channel separation is used for dual mode cellular (see 1.3.2). Mobile Stations transmit on the lower frequency band, and Base Stations transmit on the upper frequency band. Although the separation of forward and reverse channels remains at 45 MHz, a key requirement for the digital channel was the ability of the transceiver to use Time Division Duplex (TDD) transmission. TDD access allows receive and transmit bursts to occur on different channels, but the transmission and reception cannot occur simultaneously (see figure 4.4). This eliminated the need for a costly, bulky, and power inefficient duplexer when operating on a digital traffic channel.[1]

4.3.3. Modulation Type

The modulation methods employed for dual mode equipment are FM (Frequency Modulation) for voice, FSK (Frequency Shift Keying) for digital signaling on the control channels and analog voice channels, and Π/4 DQPSK modulation for transmission on digital traffic channels. Differential phase shift modulation represents digital data by shifting the relative phase of the carrier to represent digital symbols. While Π/4 DQPSK modulation has a high spectral efficiency, it occupies a constant bandwidth and may interfere with adjacent analog channels.

---

1   While the duplexer can be eliminated, most implementations of dual mode equipments will continue to use the duplexer as it is required for the analog section and control channel.

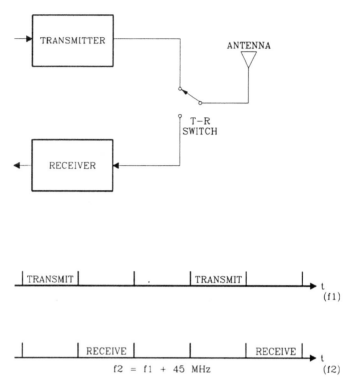

Figure 4.4 Time Division Duplex Operation

4.3.4. Digital Signal Processing

Digital signal processing for the dual mode cellular equipment includes speech data compression, error detection, and error correction procedures. Data compression is accomplished by the speech codec section where 64 kbps digital voice data is characterized and compressed into 8 kbps data. Error detection is accomplished by sending parity bits in addition to the information bits which are mathematical functions of the information. If the decoding of the received bits by the same mathematical function does not create the same received parity bits, the data was received in error. Error correction is performed by using redundant bits that can be compared by mathematical relationships to other bits. This allows the correction of a limited number of bits received in error.

4.3.5. Channel Structure

The Dual Mode cellular system has three types of channels: control channels, analog voice channels, and digital traffic channels. The control channels use FSK signaling and transfer only control information. The analog voice channel uses FM and FSK modulation to transfer voice and control signaling information. Digital traffic channels are divided into time slots and use Π/4 DQPSK modulation to transfer voice and control signaling information. Each user is assigned a particular slot for its reception and transmission.

Figure 4.5 shows that each 20 msec speech signal is converted to 6.67 msec data bursts. This is accomplished by digitizing the analog signal, processing the digital signal to reduce the number of bits required, and time compressing the data bits. The data bits are then interleaved between adjacent 20 msec time slots prior to phase modulating the RF carrier.

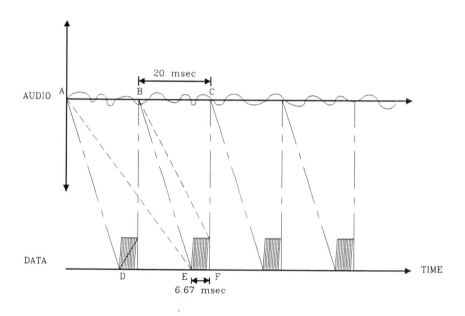

Figure 4.5 Speech Data Compression

The RF channel is divided into six time slots. The six time slots are grouped together to form frames. Channels can be classified as full rate or half rate. A full rate channel allows the Mobile Station to use two of the six slots for transmit, two for receive, and two are idle. Figure 4.6 shows the time layout of how the full rate channel is used.

A half rate channel uses one slot for transmit, one for receive, and four are idle. Figure 4.7 displays how the half rate channel structure can be set up. The half rate channel has a much lower data throughput although it allows for more users to share the channel. Figures 4.6 & 4.7 show the time relationship of the RF channels. Transmit and receive slots occur on different frequencies (see figure 4.4). As with the analog channel structure, the mobile station receive frequency is 45 MHz above the transmit frequency.

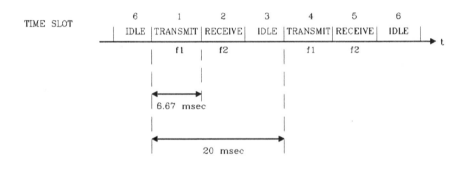

Figure 4.6 Full Rate Channel Structure

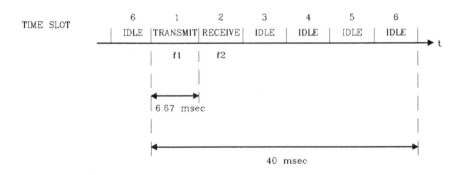

Figure 4.7 Half Rate Channel Structure

4.4. SYSTEM OPERATION

The dual mode cellular system consists of three basic elements: Mobile Stations (analog and dual mode), Base Stations (analog and dual mode), and a MSC (Mobile Switching Center). Dual Mode Mobile Stations and Base Stations differ from their analog predecessors as they have analog and digital transmission capability. Although the MSC does not have to be physically different, some equipment configurations will result in MSC changes for the dual mode cellular system.

Mobile Stations communicate by RF energy to the Base Station via analog or digital RF channels. Base Stations convert these radio signals for transfer to the MSC via land line or alternate communication links. The MSC routes the call to another Mobile Station in the system or the appropriate land line facility.

A Mobile Station initializes when first powered on by scanning dedicated control channels and tuning to the strongest signal. The Mobile Station then enters an Initialization Mode to retrieve system identification and setup information. After initialization, the Mobile Station enters the Idle Mode where it waits for its phone number to be received (paging) or the user to originate a call (access). When a call is to be received or originated, the Mobile Station attempts to access the system via a control channel. The Mobile Station then enters the System Access Mode where it competes for access and performs an authentication procedure to validate its ESN (Electronic Serial Number). If access is successful, the MSC sends out an IVCD (Initial Voice Channel Designation) message or ITCD (Initial Traffic Channel Designation) message. The Mobile Station then tunes to the RF voice channel if an analog channel is assigned (IVCD) or an RF digital traffic channel and time slot if a digital channel is assigned (ITCD). The Mobile Station then enters the Conversation Mode. When the Mobile Station operates on an RF analog voice channel, the system uses FM (Frequency Modulation) which is similar to commercial FM radio broadcast stations. Mobile Stations operating on the digital traffic channel use phase modulation. This phase modulation contains digital error detection and correction capability similar to what is used on compact discs. When control messages are required to be sent on the voice or traffic channel, digital messages replace the voice information for a short burst.

4.4.1. Access

When a Mobile Station attempts to obtain service from a cellular system, it is referred to as "access." Mobile Stations compete to obtain access. Mobile Stations attempt access when a command is received by the Mobile Station that indicates the system needs to service the Mobile Station (such as a call to be received) or as a result of a request from the user to originate a call. Access is performed by the Mobile Station monitoring the busy/idle status of the control channel before and during the transmission of an access attempt message. If the channel is available, it will begin to transmit while simultaneously monitoring the status of the control channel. The channel must become busy within the prescribed time limit or the access attempt must stop as it is assumed another Mobile Station has gained attention of the Base Station.

For the dual mode Mobile Station operating in a system which has digital capability, it must perform an authentication procedure to validate its ESN. The authentication algorithm combines several sources of information including an SSD (Shared Secret Data) to encrypt the ESN prior to transmission.

When an access attempt is successful, the system sends out the IVCD or ITCD message assigning this particular Mobile Station to a cellular voice or digital traffic channel. If the attempt has failed, the Mobile Station waits a random time before attempting access again.

4.4.2. Paging

A call reaches the Mobile Station by the process of paging. A page occurs when a message is sent on the control channel which contains the Mobile Station's identification number (Phone Number) indicating a call is to be received. If the Mobile Station is active in the system and wishes to receive the call, it responds to the page by attempting access to the system. The Mobile Station sends a message during the access attempt indicating the access is a result of the paging operation.

4.5. FUNCTIONAL DESCRIPTION

Mobile Stations, Base Stations, and MSC equipment are integrated to form a ubiquitous coverage radio system that can connect to the Public Switched Telephone Network (PSTN). The Mobile Station provides access between the subscriber and the cellular system. Base Stations provide the interface between the Mobile Station and the MSC. The MSC coordinates the operation of the cellular network and routes communications links to the

PSTN. Dual mode cellular systems differ from analog systems as Mobile Stations and Base Stations have both analog and digital transmission capability and two MSCs may be used to allow quick system implementation.

4.5.1. Mobile Station

A Mobile Station contains a transceiver, control head, and antenna assembly (see figure 4.8). The transceiver converts audio to RF and RF into audio. A control head provides the display and keypad which allow the subscriber to communicate commands to the transceiver. RF energy is focused and converted for transmission and reception into free space by the antenna assembly. Subscriber operation of the Dual Mode Mobile Station is identical to an Analog Mobile Station although the transceiver section has changed significantly.

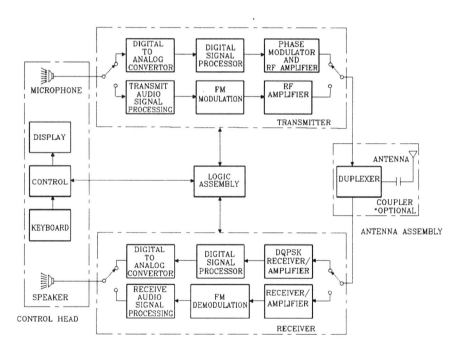

Figure 4.8 Dual Mode Mobile Station Block Diagram

4.5.1.1. Transceiver

The transceiver consists of transmitter, receiver, and logic sections. The transmitter converts low level audio signals to shifts in the RF carrier frequency and phase. The receiver amplifies and demodulates low level RF signals into their original audio form. And the logic section coordinates this operation by the insertion and extraction of system control messages. The dual mode transceiver is capable of processing both analog FM and digital Π/4 DQPSK modulated signals.

Transmitter

The transmitter consists of analog and digital processing sections. The analog processing section operates as defined in the EIA-553 specification. Sections unique to the digital transmitter include: analog to digital conversion, speech codec, channel coder, Π/4 DQPSK modulator, and a linear RF amplifier.

The analog to digital convertor changes audio signals into 64 kbps PCM digital form. The speech codec characterizes and compresses the 64 kbps data into 8 kbps. The channel coder inserts error detection, error correction, and signaling information. The Π/4 DQPSK modulator changes the data into proportional phase shift changes in the RF carrier. Finally, the linear RF amplifier boosts the output of the modulator for transmission.

The transmitter is capable of adjusting its power levels to transmit only the necessary power to be received by the Base Station. To conserve battery life in portables and transportables, the RF amplifier may turn off its power during periods where the Mobile Station operator is not talking.

Only a few sections of the transmitter can be common to both the analog and digital processing sections. These include audio preamplifier and the linear RF amplifier.[2]

Receiver

The receiver consists of analog and digital processing sections. The analog receiver processing section operates as defined in the EIA-553 specification. Sections unique to the digital receiver include: RF amplifier, demodulator, equalizer, channel decoder, speech decoder, and analog to digital conversion.

---

2   A linear amplifier is less efficient than the class C amplifiers used for FM transmission. Therefore it is unlikely the same RF amplifier will be used for both analog and digital signals.

The RF amplifier boosts the low level RF signal to a level appropriate for input to the demodulator. The demodulator converts proportional frequency (phase) changes into digital data. An equalizer section adjusts the receiver section to compensate for the phase and amplitude distortions created by the transmission path of the radio signal. The channel decoder separates signaling commands from speech data and detects and corrects bit errors. The speech decoder converts the compressed 8 kbps data back into 64 kbps PCM digital data. Finally, the digital to analog convertor changes the digital speech data into its original audio signals.

Logic Section

The logic section contains a microprocessor operating from stored program memory to coordinate the operation of the transmitter and receiver sections. The logic section inserts and extracts control messages, changes physical parameters (such as channel frequencies), and communicates with the control head to allow the subscriber to command the phone. Control signals are analog (FM), digital (FSK), and digital Π/4 DQPSK, and must be inserted into the transmitter section and extracted from the receiver section. The logic section encodes and decodes control signals and performs the call processing procedures.

4.5.1.2. Control Head

The control head consists of audio, display and keypad assemblies and may have optional interfaces such as user data transfer, hands free, and voice activation. The control head for a Dual Mode Mobile Station may not be different than an Analog control head.

The audio interface assembly consists of a speaker and microphone. The display assembly allows for preoriginating dialing, provides for updating the transceiver status to the subscriber, and displays incoming messages.[3] The keypad allows the user to enter information to control the phone. Optional features include hands free operation and user data interface. Hands free operation may be complicated when the transceiver is operating in the digital mode as digital processing creates a 100 msec delay and echoes may by significantly noticed. The control head sometimes offers an option for a user to connect a facsimile or modem to the cellular phone. While the audio frequency range on the cellular radio channel is the same as the PSTN, when in the digital mode, complex audio (such as modem and facsimile signals)

---

3   A new feature of the dual mode transceiver is the ability to display a calling number.

cannot be directly transmitted through the codec section. Another optional feature includes voice activation which allows calls to be dialed and controlled by voice commands. More detailed description of the control head can be found in 1.6.2.

4.5.1.3. Antenna Assembly

The antenna assembly provides two essential functions. It matches the impedance of the transceiver to that of free space, and it focuses the transmission into a desired direction. Since the frequency band and power levels for the Dual Mode equipment remain the same, the same antenna assemblies can be used. For more detailed information on antenna assemblies, see 1.6.3.

4.5.2. Base Station

A Base Station consists of analog and digital transceivers, control sections, RF combiner, communication links, analog scanning receiver, digital scanning receiver,[4] backup power supplies, RF test and alarm equipment, and an antenna assembly. The transceiver sections are similar to the Mobile Station transceiver sections, converting audio to RF signals and RF to audio signals. The control sections coordinate the operation of the Base Station and its communication links. The RF combiner allows the sharing of an antenna assembly by the bandpass filtering of radio channels between multiple transceivers. Communication links route audio and control information between the Base Station and MSC. Scanning receivers provide the capability of measuring the mobiles' signal strength on any of the analog or digital cellular channels. The backup power supply maintains operation when primary power is interrupted. Many of the sections within the Base Station will be duplicated in the event of equipment failure.

The dual mode Base Station may share some of the resources needed by analog base stations. Due to the optional location of some of the digital processing sections in the MSC, actual equipment configurations may vary significantly. The key dual mode base station equipment differences include the need for a linear RF amplifier, digital transceivers, and digital scanning receiver.

---

4   The digital scanning receiver may not be needed if the Base Station commands the Mobile Station to measure the channel quality of potential cell site radio channels for handoff.

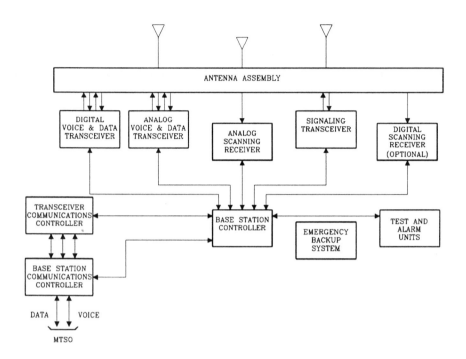

Figure 4.9 Dual Mode Base Station Block Diagram

4.5.2.1. Transceivers

There are analog and digital[5] transceivers in a dual mode Base Station. Analog transceivers are used for the control channel and analog voice channels. Digital transceivers are used only for digital traffic channels. Transceivers are composed of Transmitter, Receiver, and Logic sections. Each analog transceiver section provides for one communication channel. Each digital transceiver provides for 3 communications channels when serving full rate Mobile Stations and up to 6 channels when half rate transmission is supported.

---

5   Some transceivers may be dual mode (switchable) between analog and digital.

Transmitter

There are analog and digital transmitter types within the base station. The analog transmitter section operates as defined in the EIA-553 specification (see 1.6.4.1). Sections unique to the digital transmitter include: speech codec, channel coder,[6] Π/4 DQPSK modulator, and a linear RF amplifier.

An analog to digital convertor is not needed as the communications link already has the audio in PCM digital form.[7] The speech codec characterizes and compresses the 64 kbps data into 8 kbps. The channel coder inserts error detection, error correction, and signaling information. The Π/4 DQPSK modulator changes the data into proportional phase shift changes in the RF carrier. Finally, the linear RF amplifier boosts the output of the modulator for transmission and normally does not change output power.[8]

Receiver

There are analog and digital receivers in a dual mode Base Station. Each type of receiver has audio processing, modulation, and RF power amplifier. The analog receiver section conforms to EIA-553 (see 1.6.4.1). Sections unique to the digital receiver include: RF amplifier, demodulator, equalizer, channel decoder, speech decoder, and analog to digital conversion.

The RF amplifier boosts the low level RF signal to a level appropriate for input to the demodulator. The demodulator converts proportional frequency (phase) changes into digital data. An equalizer section adjusts the receiver section to compensate for the phase and amplitude distortions created by the transmission path of the radio signal. The channel decoder separates signaling commands from speech data and detects and corrects bit errors. The speech decoder converts the compressed 8 kbps data back into 64 kbps PCM digital data. A digital to analog convertor is not needed as the communications link already has the audio in PCM digital form.

---

6 The speech coder and channel coder may be located at the MSC.

7 It is possible to connect base station communication links to analog telephone lines which would require an A/D convertor. This is highly unlikely.

8 Digital channels may support dynamic power control and adjust their power on a frame by frame basis.

Logic

The logic section of the Base Station consists of control signal routing and message processing. Audio and digital signaling messages are inserted and extracted from the radio channel on command of the controller section. Digital messages are encoded and decoded from the logic section. The logic section for the digital transceivers is much more complex as it operates at a much higher data rate, supports more messages, and coordinates up to 6 Mobile Stations on one digital traffic channel.

4.5.2.2. Controller

There are three types of Base Station controllers: Base Station controller, Base Station communications controller, and Transceiver communications controller. The Base Station controller coordinates the operation of all Base Station equipment based on commands received from the MSC. Voice and Data communications from the MSC are buffered and rate adapted by the Base Station communications controller. Digital voice information from the communications link is converted to analog (for analog transceivers) or converted to a continuous 64 kbps channel (for digital transceivers) and routed to the radios by the transceiver communications controller. Controllers provide for the insertion of control channel signaling messages, setup of voice channels, and operation of the scanning receiver. In addition, controllers monitor equipment status and provide operational and failure status to the MSC.

4.5.2.3. RF Combiner

The RF combiner consists of narrow bandpass filters that allow separate transmitters with different frequency outputs to be connected to the same antenna assembly without significant interference with each other. Since the RF channel bandwidth remains the same for dual mode equipment, the same RF combiner may be used for analog and digital transceivers.

4.5.2.4. Communications Links

Because a dual mode Base Station is capable of supporting many additional communications channels, additional communications links may be required. Communications links are often digital time multiplexed T1 (see chapter 3, T1) to increase the efficiency of the line. To prevent a single link failure from disabling communications, alternate communications should be provided [9].

Dependent on the implementation, the data compression capability of the codec may be used to allow subrate multiplexing of the existing communications links.[9] Subrate multiplexing allows more than one user to share the same communications channel by compressing information to a lower rate and multiplexing these low rate signals onto one channel.

4.5.2.5. Antenna Assembly

As described in 1.6.4.5, startup cellular systems employ omnidirectional antennas and as the system matures, directional antennas replace the original antennas for reduced interference and sectoring. Dual mode base stations may use the same antenna assembly. Due to the increased capacity and cochannel resistance to Π/4 DQPSK modulated signals, the need for sectoring may be delayed.

4.5.2.6. Scanning Receiver

As described in 1.6.4.6, the scanning receiver is used to measure Mobile Station signal strength to determine its relative distance to the Base Station. The analog scanning receiver cannot be used to measure the signal strength of a Mobile Station operating on a digital traffic channel. To measure the signal strength on a digital traffic channel, either a special digital scanning receiver must be used or the Base Station instructs the Mobile Station to return the signal strength measurements using the MAHO (see chapter 5) capability.

4.5.2.7. Backup Energy Sources

Backup energy sources include batteries and generator to supply equipment and cooling systems. Digital channels require a linear power amplifier which has less efficiency than the class C amplifiers used for analog channels. This increased power consumption is offset by the ability of each digital channel to serve up to 6 Mobile Stations. This results in fewer power requirements for a dual mode base station than an analog base station.

---

9   Astronet systems perform the channel decoding at the MSC therefore allowing three users to share one communications circuit without additional data compression equipment.

4.5.3. Mobile Switching Center

The MSC assemblies and operation is the same as described in 1.6.5. The significant difference for dual mode equipment is separate analog and digital MSCs may be used and some of the base station communication equipment may be moved to the MSC.

An overlay system of MSCs may be used to allow the rapid deployment of digital channels by permitting an overlay system (see figure 4.10) to be installed without altering analog equipment configurations. The overlay system uses the optional secondary control channels to assign Mobile Stations to digital traffic channels. The only change that is necessary is to disable operating analog voice channels that have been replaced by a digital traffic channel or secondary control channel.

To allow more efficient use of communications links, some of the channel coding equipments may be moved to the MSC. It is possible to exploit the data compression ability of the speech coder by not converting the received codec data from 8 kbps to 64 kbps PCM until it reaches the MSC. This allows up to 8 users[10] to be subrate multiplexed onto one 64 kbps DS0 connection. This reduces the need for additional communications links.

---

10 Up to 16 users may be multiplexed for half rate Mobile Stations onto one DS0.

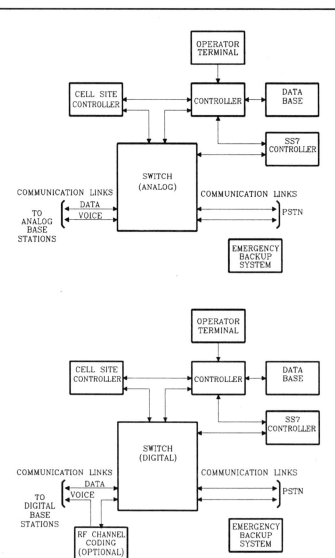

Figure 4.10 Mobile Switching Center Block Diagram

4.6. SUMMARY

The main objective of dual mode cellular is to allow cost effective capacity expansion to the existing cellular system. This is accomplished by the time sharing of the digital RF channels, ability to reuse frequencies more often, reduction of the minimum cell size, and the use of a low bit rate speech codec which performs data compression.

Key parameters of the dual mode cellular system include maintaining the same frequency allocation of 50 MHz, use of FM and DQPSK modulation, the same FSK control channel structure, and new TDMA digital traffic channels.

The dual mode cellular system has three main elements: Mobile Stations (analog and dual mode), Base Stations (analog and dual mode), and a Mobile Switching Center (MSC). The MS links the subscriber to the Base Station via FM or DQPSK radio transmission. Base Stations convert signals from Mobile Stations to signals that are relayed to the MSC. The MSC connects the cellular call to the land line network or other mobiles via BS equipment.

A dual mode MS contains a transceiver, control head, and antenna assembly. The major difference of the dual mode transceiver section is the ability to transmit both analog (FM) and digital (DQPSK) modulation and the inclusion of an ESN authentication procedure to minimize fraudulent access. Control head operation of the dual mode phone is identical. Because the frequency allocation did not change, the same antenna assembly may be used.

Dual Mode Base stations contain analog and digital transceivers, control sections, RF combiners, communication links, analog and digital scanning receivers, backup power supplies, and antenna assemblies. Differences in the dual mode base station equipment include the addition of digital transmitters and receivers, digital scanning receiver (optional), and the elimination of the digital to analog conversion between the communication links and digital transmission channels.

The MSC consists of controllers, switching assembly, communications links, operator terminals, subscriber database, and backup energy sources. Significant MSC options include separate analog and digital MSCs and configurations to reduce the number of communications links to the Base Stations. The allocation of optional control channels allows the side by side installation of MSCs (analog and digital) for quick system implementation.

More efficient use of the communications channels may result by the location of RF channel coding equipment at the MSC allowing several users to share one 64 kbps communications channel.

References:

[1] CTIA, Users' Performance Requirements, Issue 1, September 8, 1988.

[2] Electronic Industries Association, EIA Interim Standard IS-54, Rev A, "Dual-Mode Mobile Station - Base Station Compatibility Standard," March 1991.

[3] CTIA Winter Exposition, John Stupka, "Technology Update" (San Diego 1991).

[4] Dr. George Calhoun, *Digital Cellular Radio*, (MA: Artech House, 1988), pp.170-172.

[5] CTIA Industry Report, William Lee, "Effect of Co-Channel Interference on System Capacity," Volume 7, No. 4, p. 23 (April 1991).

[6] CTIA Winter Exposition, Jessee Russell, "Technology Update," Reno Nevada, February 6, 1990.

[7] CTIA Winter Exposition, Mike Callendar, "PCN: What is it and Where is it Going," Reno Nevada, February 6, 1990.

[8] CTIA Winter Exposition, John Stupka, "Technology Update," Reno Nevada, 1990.

[9] CTIA Winter Exposition, "Disaster Experiences," Reno, Nevada, February 6, 1990.

Chapter 5

Dual Mode Mobile Station

5.1. INTRODUCTION

To establish communications in a Dual Mode cellular system, Dual Mode Mobile Stations must operate within electrical parameters, conform to signaling structures, and call process signaling messages. The Dual Mode Mobile Station contains functional sections to comply with these requirements. This chapter provides a technical description of mobile station parameters, signaling structures, call processing, and functional assemblies.

5.2. DUAL MODE MOBILE STATION PARAMETERS

Mobile Stations must conform to IS-54 [1] and IS-55 [2] to ensure compatibility with the cellular system network. To allow operation of the Dual Mode Mobile Station in an analog only system, the analog section operational part contained in IS-54 was incorporated from EIA-553 [3] and the analog section minimum performance parameters part contained in IS-55 was incorporated from IS-19B [4]. These standards contain parameters for the RF channel structure, signaling, and call processing functions.

5.2.1. Channel Frequency Assignment

The 25 MHz x 2 cellular frequency allocation remains the same where the transmit band for the base station is 869-894 MHz and the transmit band for the mobile station is 824-849 MHz (see figure 1.4). All RF channels are frequency duplex (separated by 45 MHz) although digital channels divide receive and transmit frequencies into time slots which allow TDD (Time Division Duplex) operation. Analog and digital RF channels occupy a maximum of 30 kHz bandwidth.

To allow the overlay of a separate digital system on an existing analog system, and to increase control channel capacity, some of the analog voice channels may be converted to control channels. These control channels are optional and are an implementation issue.

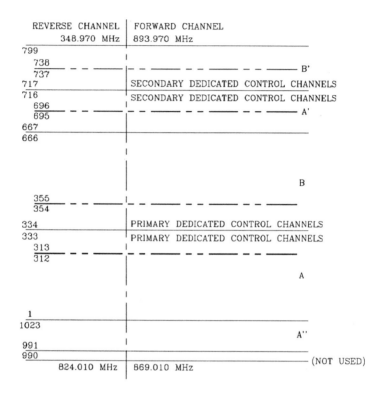

Figure 5.1 Dual Mode Channel Frequency Allocations

5.2.2. Mobile Station Power Output

A new power class of mobile, class IV, has been added which has a maximum output power of -2 dBW and a minimum power output of -34 dBW. This is identical to the Class III portable except it has an extended 12 dB range at the low end to allow reduction in minimum cell site radius.

5.2.3. Modulation

Control channels continue to use FSK modulation. Analog voice channels use both FM and FSK modulation. Digital traffic channel use $\pi/4$ DQPSK modulation. $\pi/4$ DQPSK modulation was chosen to provide enhanced spectral efficiency and optimization of the RF amplifier section. To fully understand this modulation, Phase and Quadrature modulation will be discussed.

5.2.3.1. Phase Modulation

Phase modulation is a result of the shifting of the carrier frequency above and below the carrier center frequency to introduce phase changes at specific points of time. Figure 5.2 displays a carrier frequency phase modulated by signal $v(t)$. At time 1, the carrier is at the center frequency. At time 2, the carrier is momentarily shifted above its center frequency for a short period to introduce a (-) phase shift. At time 3, the carrier is at the center frequency. Time 4 requires the carrier to go below the center frequency to introduce a $(+)$ phase shift. At time 5, the carrier is again at the center frequency.

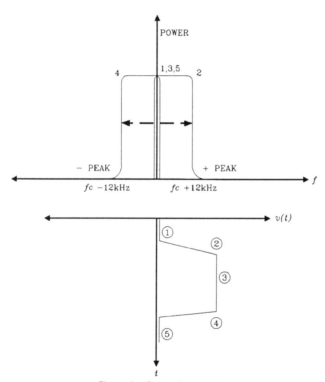

Figure 5.2 Phase Modulation

Table 5.1 provides a simple example of phase shift keying modulation. Stimulus input to a phase modulator results in a proportional phase shift in the reference carrier. If we let +1 volt result in a phase shift of 90 degrees, a +0.5 volt input will cause a 45 degree phase shift. Thus the phase shift is proportional to the input modulation signal (information). The difference between FM and PM is the change of carrier center frequency for FM is directly proportional to the amplitude of the modulating signal and the change of carrier center frequency for PM is directly proportional to the derivative of the modulating signal [5].

$$FM : \Delta f_c \alpha g(t)$$

$$PM: \Delta f_c \alpha dg(t)/dt$$

where: $g(t)$ is the modulating signal

Table 5.1 Sample Deviations

Time	Input (volts)	$\Delta\ \theta$	θ
0	0.0	0	0
1	−0.5	−π/4	−π/4
2	1.0	+3π/4	+π/2
3	1.0	0	+π/2
4	0.5	−π/4	+π/4
5	−1.0	−3π/4	−π/2
6	−1.0	0	−π/2

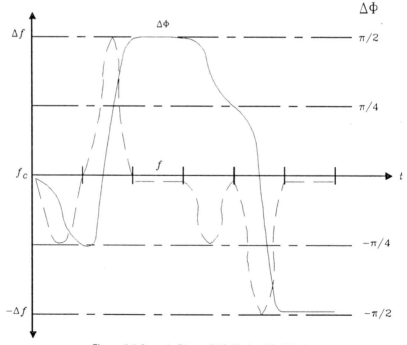

Figure 5.3 Sample Phase Shift Keying Modulation

Figure 5.3 shows the changes in phase and center frequency (fc) for the phase modulated signal contained in table 5.1.

5.2.3.2. Quadrature Phase Shift Modulation

It is possible to increase the spectral efficiency by multiplexing two signals in phase quadrature. This may be best explained by the use of an I-Q pattern where two amplitude modulated RF signals which are 90 degrees out of phase are combined. For our example, binary signals vary the amplitude of each of the two RF signals. The I axis is the amplitude of the first signal source reference amplitude varied by binary signal Xk. The Q axis is the amplitude of the 90 degree phase shifted signal modulated by binary signal Yk. The combination of the varied amplitudes results in amplitude and phase components shown on the I-Q pattern.

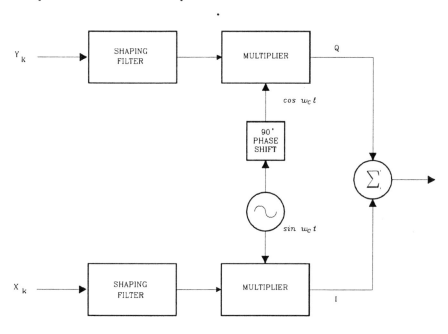

Figure 5.4 Quadrature Phase Shift Keying Modulator

For quadrature modulation, information in all four quadrants is used to impose and determine modulation information. Figure 5.5 shows four points that are the result of combining the two signals with amplitudes determined by the table in Figure 5.5.

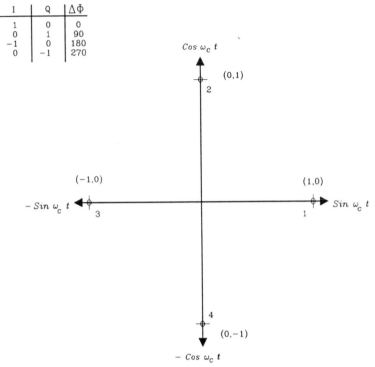

I	Q	ΔΦ
1	0	0
0	1	90
-1	0	180
0	-1	270

Figure 5.5 I-Q Pattern Coordinate System

5.2.3.3. Differential Quadrature Phase Shift Modulation

By choosing relative 45 degree and 135 degree shifts, each set of modulation information (Xk,Yk) will result in a new set of decision points. For example, if the first shift is +45 degrees and a second shift is +135 degrees the end result is +180 degrees which was not part of the original set of decision points. These shift values were chosen to allow two sets of decision points. A total of eight decision points are displayed in figure 5.6 where decision points alternate and the x's and o's mark alternating decision points. A transition from any o reference point must end at any one of the x decision points. If the resultant shift (phase change) does not reach a final value within those decision areas, the data is in error and must be corrected by using error protected bits or discarded.

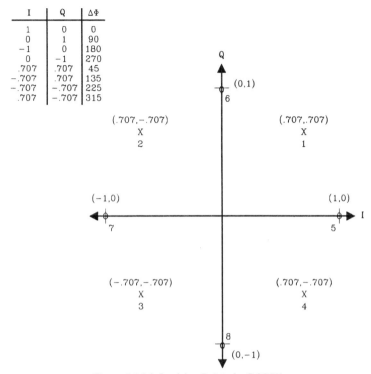

I	Q	ΔΦ
1	0	0
0	1	90
-1	0	180
0	-1	270
.707	.707	45
-.707	.707	135
-.707	-.707	225
.707	-.707	315

Figure 5.6 I-Q Decision Points for DQPSK

Several circuits may be used to phase shift an RF signal to create the decision points. One modulator type, a balanced modulator shown in figure 5.4, combines two signals that are at the same RF frequency but have a 90 degrees phase relationship. By varying the amplitude of each reference frequency (performed by the multipliers shown), the decision points can be created. For example in figure 5.7, if we start out at $s1$, the amplitude of $sin\omega_c t$ is multiplied by 1 and output and $cos\omega_c t$ is multiplied by 0. This results in all of $sin\omega_c t$ being obtained at the output. To move to $s5$, both $sin\omega_c t$ and $cos\omega_c t$ are multiplied by .707 which results in a 45 degree phase shift. Table 5.2 shows the amplitudes for each of the reference signals to create all of the decision points.

Table 5.2 IS-54 Decision Points

s1 = $A\cos\omega_c t$
s2 = $A\cos\omega_c t$
s3 = $-A\sin\omega_c t$
s4 = $-A\cos\omega_c t$
s5 = $.707A\,(\sin\omega_c t + \cos\omega_c t)$
s6 = $.707A(\cos\omega_c t - \sin\omega_c t)$
s7 = $-.707A(\sin\omega_c t + \cos\omega_c t)$
s8 = $-.707A\,(\cos\omega_c t - \sin\omega_c t)$

Any s1-4 starting point must transition to one of s5-8 end points, and any s5-8 starting point must transition to one of s1-4 end points.

For the IS-54 $\pi/4$ DQPSK modulation, with each two bit stimulus input, a corresponding phase shift occurs. Figure 5.7 shows all the possible decision point transitions from s1. Gray coding is used between decision points so only a one bit error may occur between decision points errors (IS-54, p. 20).

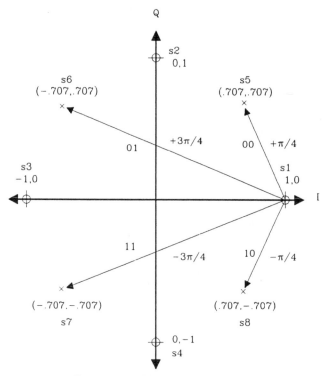

Figure 5.7 $\pi/4$ DQPSK State Transitions

5.2.4. RF Channel Structure

There are three types of channels for a dual mode cellular system. The first type of channel is a control channel which performs paging and channel assignment. The second type of channel is an analog voice channel which transfers information by FM and FSK modulation. The third type of channel is a digital traffic channel which performs the same function as the analog voice channel but uses time division multiplexing and DQPSK modulation.

The dual mode system allocates the same dedicated control channels (now termed primary dedicated control channels) as the EIA-553 standard with the addition of a new band of optional dedicated control channels (now termed secondary dedicated control channels). The primary dedicated control channels remain for the A service provider are 313 to 333 and for the B service provider are 334 to 354. The secondary dedicated control channels for the A service provider are 696 to 716 and for the B service provider 717 to 737 (see figure 5.1).

The dual mode analog voice channel performs all of the functions associated with the analog voice channel as defined in EIA-553. A new handoff message has been created for the analog channel which transfers the extra parameters (time slot number) necessary for an analog to digital traffic channel handoff. It is anticipated that new features will be added to the analog voice channel to support some of the new digital channel features [6].

Digital traffic channels are time division multiplexed (TDM) into frames and time slots. Frames are 40 msec and consist of 6 time slots. There are two types of user channel assignments, full rate and half rate. A full rate channel uses 2 of the 6 slots for transmit, 2 for receive, and 2 are idle. To double the RF channel capacity, eventually half rate channels will be used where the mobile uses 1 of the 6 slots for transmit, 1 for receive, and 4 will remain idle. Each RF digital channel transports a gross bit rate of 48.6 kbps. Subtracting control data and dividing the number of slots used per user, this results in a user available data rate of 13 kbps for full rate and less than 6.5 kbps for half rate (due to an increased percentage of signaling data requirements). While not yet specified, Sub Rate and Superframe Structures are anticipated so that rates of less than 1 of 6 slots and more than 2 of 6 slots will be supported in the future to allow alternate data rates dependent on user requirements.

There are three types of slot structures that exist in the standard: forward speech slot, reverse speech slot, and shortened burst slot (see figures 5.8 through 5.10). Each slot type has dedicated fields and slots are composed of 324 bits (162 symbols). The fields within the slot structures are defined as:

Guard Time - A guard time is allocated to prevent the overlapping of received bursts due to radio signal transit time. The amount of guard time was minimized by using dynamic time alignment which adjusts the relative timing for the start of transmit based on the distance of the mobile from the base station.

Ramp Time - Impulse response (rapid transient) is not allowed to maintain transmission within the allocated bandwidth. The ramp time allows gradual rising and falling of RF energy within each transmit burst.

Data - The data bits are the transmitted information that will be processed. The data bits are interleaved and error protected.

Sync Word - The synchronization word allows time alignment and training of the equalizer.

SACCH - The SACCH allows out of band signaling at very low rates. 12 dedicated bits per time slot have been allocated for slow channel signaling information.

CDVCC - The DVCC (Digital Voice Color Code) is appended with 4 parity bits to form the 12 bit CDVCC (Coded Digital Voice Color Code). This color code provides the co-channel interference identification in a similar manner to the SAT code.

Figure 5.8 shows the slot structure for a forward data slot. The forward data slot transfers voice and data from the base station to the mobile station. No guard time is needed as the Base Station continuously transmits on all slots.

28	12	130	12	130	12
S	SA	DATA	D	DATA	RSV

```
NOTE:    S  -IS SYNCHRONIZATION WORD
        SA  -IS SACCH
      DATA  -IS USER INFORMATION
         D  -IS CODED DIGITAL TRAFFIC COLOR CODE
       RSV  -IS RESERVED
```

Figure 5.8 Forward Traffic Channel Slot Structure

Figure 5.9 shows the slot structure for a reverse data slot. The reverse data slot transfers voice and data from the mobile station to the base station. This differs from the forward data slot as it must include a guard time and ramp time.

6	6	16	28	122	12	12	122
G1	RA	DATA	S	DATA	SA	D	DATA

NOTE: S   –IS SYNCHRONIZATION WORD
SA –IS SACCH
DATA –IS USER INFORMATION
D   –IS CODED DIGITAL TRAFFIC COLOR CODE
RSV –IS RESERVED
G1 –IS STANDARD GUARD TIME
RA –IS RAMP UP TIME

Figure 5.9 Reverse Traffic Channel Slot Structure

Figure 5.10 shows the shortened burst slot structure. Shortened bursts (slots) are sent when a mobile station begins operating in a large diameter cell because the propagation time between the mobile and base is unknown. Although dynamic time alignment is provided, the base must determine how much offset is necessary. Initially, the mobile transmits shortened burst slots until the base can calculate the required offset.

6	6	28	12	4	28	12	8	28	12	12	28	12	16	28	22
G1	RA	S	D	V	S	D	W	S	D	X	S	D	Y	S	G2

NOTE: G1 –IS STANDARD GUARD TIME
S   –IS SYNCHRONIZATION WORD
D   –IS DTCC
V   –IS 0H
W   –IS 00H
X   –IS 000H
Y   –IS 0000H
G2 –IS ADDITIONAL GUARD TIME
RA –IS RAMP UP TIME

Figure 5.10 Shortened Burst Slot Structure

Figure 5.11 shows how burst overlap may occur due to propagation time. Shortened burst transmission is initially required in large diameter cells where the propagation time is long and overlap may occur. Once the propagation time can be determined, the mobile station advances its transmit burst start time in relation to the received slot based on commands received from the base station. The required timing offset is two times the path delay. This is due to the delay for the receive and then delay for the transmit. The default delay between the receive and transmit slots in the mobile is 44 symbols. This difference can be reduced in 1/2 symbol increments up to 15 symbols (30 increments). A guard time of 3 symbols was established to eliminate the need for time alignment in small radius cells. This results in the maximum distance the mobile can operate from the base station is 72 miles before slot collisions (burst overlap) will occur.

Path propagation delay = 5.3 *μsec/mi*

Round trip delay   = 10.6 *μsec/mi*

One symbol = 41.1 *μsec* = 1/2 *symbol* = 20.55 *μsec*

2 miles require 1/2 symbol = >12 *miles* = 3 *symbols*

The standard guard time is 3 symbols

Maximum distance = 12 *mi* + *(4 mi/symbol* x 15 *symbols)* = 72 *mi*

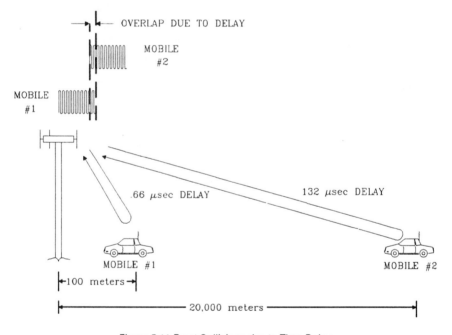

Figure 5.11 Burst Collisions due to Time Delay

5.3. SIGNALING

Given the physical RF channel parameters, a mobile station communicates with the cellular system by sending signaling messages. Signaling message formats vary between control channels, voice channels, and traffic channels. Control channel signaling is all FSK digital; voice channel signaling is a mixture of digital messages and audio tones; and traffic channel signaling is DQPSK digital.

5.3.1. Control Channel Signaling

Control channel signaling continues to use FSK (Frequency Shift Keying). The difference between the control channel signaling for Analog and Dual Mode mobiles are: a dedicated bit indicates if the base has digital capability, a new band of secondary dedicated control channels, additional parameters for assignment to a digital traffic channel, and a reversal of separate paging and access channel functions.

A new field, Protocol Capability Indicator (PCI), is sent in the overhead messages which indicates the Base Station has digital capability. If the Mobile Station does not find the PCI field to indicate digital capability, the MS may search for the optional secondary band of control channels (696-737) to determine if they exist to support digital channels. A new message has been added, ITCD (initial traffic channel designator), which contains parameters necessary for assignment to a digital traffic channel. These parameters include channel number, time slot, and type of channel indicator (full or half rate). To increase the capacity of the primary control channels (313-354) when separate paging and access channels are used, the dual mode MS will respond to pages on the access channel and attempt access on the paging channels.

5.3.2. Analog Voice Channel Signaling

Operation on the Analog voice channel is identical to the original EIA-553 standard with the addition of new messages to support handoff to digital traffic channels. It is expected that new orders will be created to allow the advanced features of the digital traffic channel (e.g. calling number identification). Existing analog mobile stations will not respond to these advanced features as orders received that cannot be correctly decoded must be discarded [7].

5.3.3. Digital Traffic Channel Signaling

The physical method of signaling on the digital traffic channel is completely changed although the signaling is functionally equivalent. DTMF signaling is performed by a combination of in band and out of band signaling. The functional equivalent of SAT is CDVCC which allows a Base Station signal to be echoed back indicating a reliable radio path is being maintained. As discussed in chapter 4, transferring control messages on the digital traffic channel is performed by two channels, FACCH and SACCH. The FACCH channel replaces speech with control signal data and the SACCH channel transfers messages by dedicated bits within each burst. FACCH message signaling is similar to the blank and burst signaling where speech information is replaced with control data when control messages are sent.

5.3.3.1. DTMF

DTMF signals are used to control equipments connected to the PSTN such as voice mail, answering machines, bank services, etc. Originally, DTMF signals were not anticipated to be capable of being passed via the codec (dual mode digital speech processing section). Testing has shown that DTMF tones can be passed through the codec [8]. Unfortunately, the codec adds twist distortion. Twist distortion is the amplitude relationship between one tone component to another tone component within the DTMF signal. The situation could be made further complex if data compression devices (other codecs) are used between the cell site and MTSO which also use codecs. Figure 5.12 shows how DTMF signals are created and what the twist distortion limit is.

5.3.3.2. CDVCC

To ensure reliable control of the Mobile Station (a quality RF channel), a CDVCC field is echoed back in a similar method to the SAT tone. CDVCC is composed of an 8 bit DVCC word appended with 4 parity check bits. This results in 255 unique codes which is much more than the three possible SAT frequencies.[1] Figure 5.13 displays how the CDVCC field is transponded back to the Base Station.

---

[1]   The combination 00h is not used which reduces the unique DVCC words from 256 to 255.

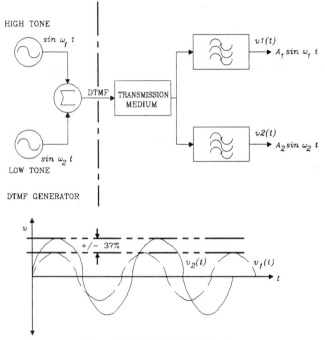

Figure 5.12 DTMF Twist Distortion

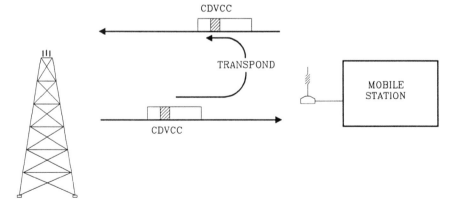

Figure 5.13 Transponding DVCC

5.3.3.3. FACCH

FACCH messages replace speech data with control signal messages. No limit has been established on how many speech frames may be replaced and the speech coder voice quality degradation with lost frames is non-linear.

FACCH messages replace speech frames (260 bits), are interleaved, and a message is composed over two slots (see figure 5.14). The gross FACCH transmission rate is 13 kbps (for a full rate channel) and the data is error protected by a 1/4 rate convolution coder. This reduces the net transmission rate to 3250 bps. Messages include a CF flag and CRC parity check bits. Subtraction of these fields results in a transmission rate of :

– 2.4 kbps throughput full rate

–1.2 kbps net throughput half rate[2]

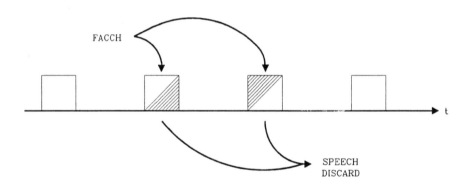

Figure 5.14 FACCH Signaling

---

2   Half rate signaling has not been established. The actual data rate may vary dependent on the designated channel structure.

FACCH messages are 1/4 rate convolutional encoded to allow extra error protection. It is probable that FACCH messages will be necessary to control the mobile in poor radio conditions (such as handoff). Each FACCH message uses 49 bits. This is allocated according to the following format:

CF	MESSAGE
1	48

Where: CF = Continuation Flag

MESSAGE = data bits

Figure 5.15 shows how a coded FACCH message is created. First, the CRC is generated by preceding the DVCC to the message. This bit sequence is passed into the CRC generator which creates a 16 bit CRC field. The resultant CRC field is appended to the original message without the DVCC field. This composite bit sequence is fed into the 1/4 rate convolutional coder which its output is placed into an array for interleaving prior to transmission. Similar to speech, FACCH data is interleaved to reduce the effects of burst errors.

There are no fields within a standard slot which identifies it as speech data or a FACCH message. To determine if a FACCH message has been sent, the mobile must attempt to decode the slot as speech. If it decodes in error, it must then attempt to decode the slot as a FACCH slot. If the CRC then calculates correctly, it is a FACCH message.

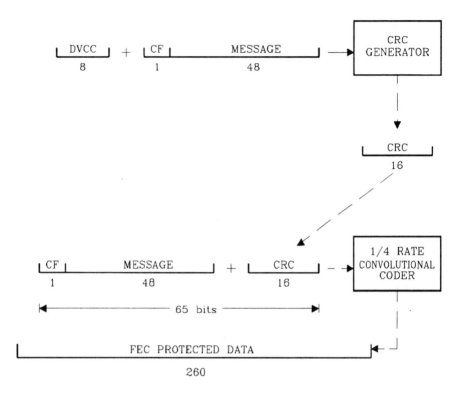

Figure 5.15 Message Coding

5.3.3.4. SACCH

A SACCH channel is provided to transmit messages in parallel without replacing speech information. A SACCH channel is made possible by the dedication of 12 bits per slot so information may be sent while speech information is processed uninterrupted (see figures 5.8 and 5.9). A balance was maintained to allow the maximum number of bits to be devoted to speech and to allocate a minimum number of bits to continuous signaling. Due to the minimal number of bits dedicated to SACCH messages, transferring messages is very slow. To send messages rapidly, it is possible to send some SACCH messages as FACCH messages. SACCH has a long delay that requires 22 slots as opposed to 2 slots to send one FACCH message.

Although the SACCH channel is allocated twelve bits per slot and a message contains 132 bits, SACCH messages are diagonally interleaved so a message is composed over 22 slots (see figure 5.16). The gross transmission rate is 600 bps for a full rate channel and the data is 1/2 rate convolution coded which reduces the net data transmission rate to 300 bps. Each message includes a CF flag, reserved bit, and CRC parity check bits. Subtraction of these fields results in transmission rates of:

– 218 bps throughput full rate

–109 bps throughput half rate[3]

---

3 Due to the limited number of bits available for half rate speech, the SACCH channel may be eliminated.

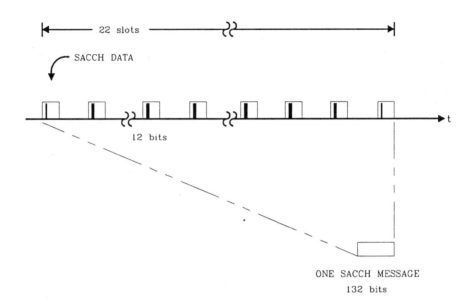

Figure 5.16 SACCH Signaling

Each SACCH message contains 50 bits. This is allocated according to the following format:

CF	RSV	MESSAGE
1	1	48

Where: CF = Continuation Flag

RSV = Reserved (set to '0')

MESSAGE = data bits

Figure 5.17 shows how a coded SACCH message is created. First, a 16 bit CRC is generated by preceding the DVCC to the message and supplying this bit sequence into the CRC generator. The resultant CRC field is appended to the original SACCH message without the DVCC field. This composite bit sequence is fed into the 1/2 rate convolutional coder. Its output is placed into an array for interleaving prior to transmission. SACCH data is then interleaved to reduce the effects of burst errors.

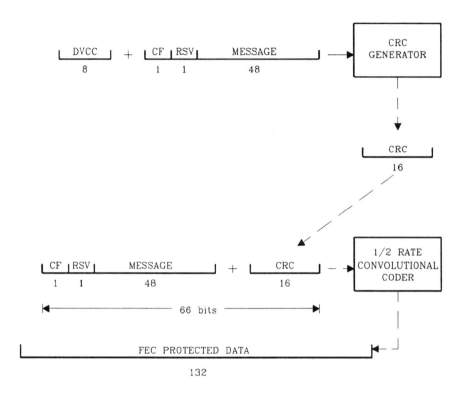

NOTE: CF   —IS CONTINUATION FLAG
       DVCC —IS DIGITAL VOICE COLOR CODE
       CRC —IS CYCLIC REDUNDANCY CHECK PARITY BITS

Figure 5.17 SACCH Message Coding

5.4. CALL PROCESSING

The primary differences for dual mode call processing are secondary control channels, reversed paging and access functions, and signaling on the digital traffic channel. To increase control channel capacity, some of the analog voice channels may be converted to a secondary band of control channels. If the mobile cannot find digital capability on the primary dedicated control channels, it may search the secondary dedicated control channels to see if they are active. If the mobile cannot receive a system message on these secondary control channels (it may be a voice channel), it must attempt access by operating as an analog mobile on the primary dedicated control channel. To increase the efficiency of control channels, when separate paging and access channels are defined and while using the primary dedicated control channels, the dual mode mobile will reverse its paging and access channels.

Call processing functions are divided into four tasks: initialization, idle, access, and conversation. The Mobile Station must first perform the Initialization task to obtain system parameters. It then remains in the Idle task where it waits for new system information, pages, or the operator to initiate a call. Once a call is initiated or a page message is received, the Mobile Station enters the System Access task where it competes for assignment to a voice channel and performs an authentication procedure. Once the system has assigned a voice channel, the Mobile Station enters the Conversation task.

5.4.1. Initialization

The mobile station obtains parameters necessary to establish communications by retrieving system overhead information which is continuously sent on control channels. The dual mode mobile station first scans the primary dedicated control channels (original EIA-553 control channels), locks on to the strongest signal, and verifies digital capability (PCI bit set). If the control channels do not indicate digital capability, the Mobile Station scans the secondary dedicated control channels. For the A service provider, these channels are 696 to 716. For the B service provider, these channels are 717 to 737. After the mobile station tunes to the strongest RF channel, it attempts to decode control channel messages. If none can be decoded, secondary control channels do not exist and the mobile once again tunes to the primary dedicated control channels and operates as an analog only mobile (see figure 5.18).

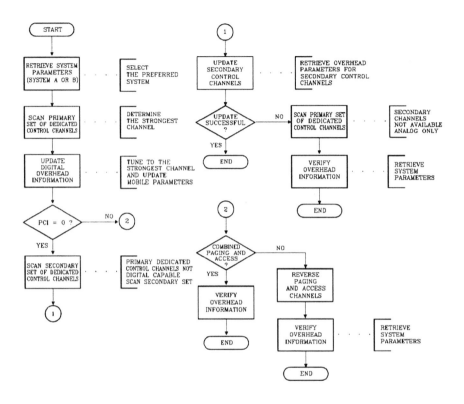

Figure 5.18 Initialization Task

When a primary dedicated control channel indicates digital capability and separate paging and access control channels exist, the mobile will listen for pages on the access channel and attempt access on the paging channels (see figure 5.19).

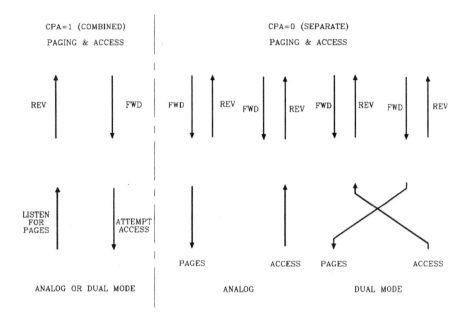

Figure 5.19 Reversed Paging and Access Channels

5.4.2. Idle

The mobile performs the idle task (figure 5.20) to continuously monitor system parameters and determine if it has been paged, received an order, or if the operator is initiating a call. System parameters may change or the mobile station may have moved to a new system that has different parameters. Pages indicate telephone numbers that are called which are sent on the control channel so active mobiles may respond and answer their calls. Orders such as registration requests are sent on the control channel for which the mobile station must continuously decode and respond to. The control part of the mobile station is monitored to determine if the operator has commanded the unit to initiate a call. The mobile station may also be requested to register with the system to determine if it is active in a particular cell site area.

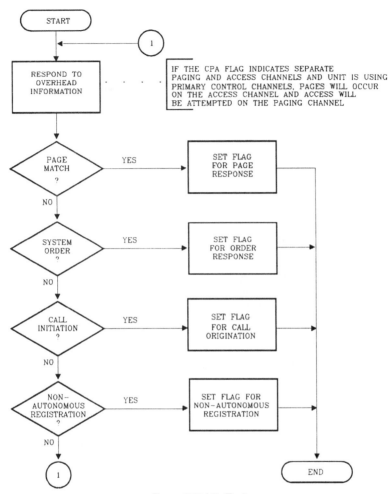

Figure 5.20 Idle Task

5.4.3. System Access Task

A mobile competes to gain the attention of the system by performing the system access task. When system access has been accomplished, the base station assigns a digital traffic channel if available. If digital channels are not available, the base station will assign the mobile to an analog voice channel.

Analog and dual mode system access functions are very similar although there are some differences (figure 5.21). Refer to section 2.4.3 and figures 2.10 and 2.11 for more detailed system access descriptions and flow diagrams.

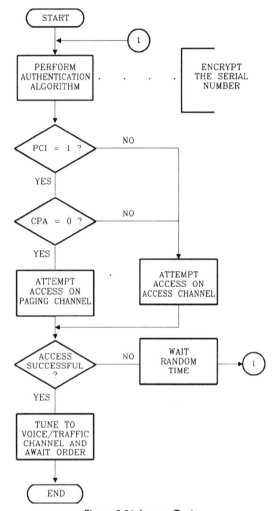

Figure 5.21 Access Task

The most significant change is the addition of an authentication procedure which is performed during access. The AUTH procedure encrypts (scrambles) the ESN based on information received from the overhead messages and stored secret data. As discussed in section 5.4.1, when separate paging and access channels are used on the primary control channels, the mobile station will attempt access on the paging channel.

5.4.4. Conversation Mode

Conversation may take place on analog voice channels or digital traffic channels. The difference between the mobile station operation on the digital traffic channel is the addition of messages to support new features. Figure 5.22 shows how messages are received and processed on the digital traffic channel. Refer to section 2.4.4 and figure 2.12 for a more detailed description and functional flow diagram for the analog voice channel.

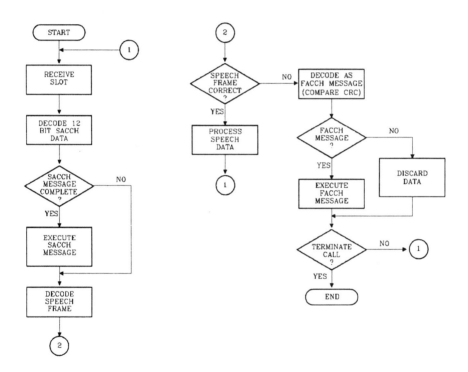

Figure 5.22 Conversation Task

Two types of messages are sent on the digital traffic channel. SACCH messages are sent in parallel with speech information. FACCH messages replace speech information. Decoding of these messages is performed in parallel as SACCH and FACCH messages will not interfere with each other.

5.5. DUAL MODE MOBILE STATION

The mobile station consists of three elements: a transceiver, antenna, and control head. The dual mode mobile transceiver requires additional transmit, receive, and control sections. Figure 5.23 shows a block diagram of a dual mode transceiver digital section. A dual mode transceiver contains both analog and digital transceiver sections. The block diagram shown in figure 2.13 must also be incorporated with figure 5.23 to complete the dual mode mobile station. Discussion of the functional sections in this chapter is limited to the digital portion of the dual mode mobile. For more detailed descriptions of analog processing, refer to section 2.5. The blocks shown are used to indicate functional sections. Some of the blocks described are implementation specific. The antenna and control head sections need not change for a dual mode mobile.

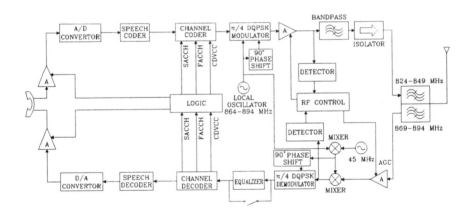

Figure 5.23 Dual Mode (Digital) Transceiver Block Diagram

5.5.1. Transceiver

The transceiver section contains transmit, receive, and logic assemblies. The transmit assembly converts low level audio signals to digitally coded RF signals by audio processing, digital signal processing, modulation and RF amplification. The receive assembly transforms low level π/4 DQPSK modulated RF signals to filtered audio signals by a low level RF amplification, demodulation, digital signal processing, and audio processing. The logic section coordinates this operation by insertion and extraction of system control messages.

5.5.1.1. Transmit Audio Processing

The transmit audio processing section converts analog signals to standard PCM data at 64 kbps. The audio is first passed through a filter to prevent aliasing distortion of the input signal. The audio waveform signal is then sampled at a rate of 8 kHz and digitized into standard u-Law 64 kbps PCM data. No compressor or emphasis circuitry is necessary for the audio processing as all audio characterization is completed in the transmitter digital signal processing section. Figure 5.24 displays the basic conversion process.

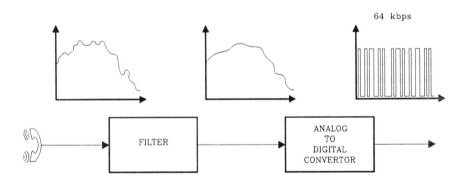

Figure 5.24 Audio Processing Block Diagram

5.5.1.2. Transmitter Digital Signal Processing (DSP)

The transmitter DSP section converts 64 kbps PCM data to a lower data rate, multiplexes control data, and error protects the data for the rapid changing RF channel. Data is compressed by the speech codec section, several channels are multiplexed together, and various methods of error detection/correction bits are created by channel coding.

Speech Codec

The speech codec section (figure 5.25) compresses the 64 kbps PCM data into 7950 bps data. It is important to understand that the speech coding data compression does not reproduce all complex audio information presented to it. The speech codec optimizes data compression based on the human voice signal characteristics. Therefore, it is unable to track rapidly changing phase shifted audio signals such as modem data. Consequently, an alternate method has been incorporated to send facsimile and modem data through the network.

The codec selected for the full rate IS-54 channel is a VSELP (Vector Sum Linear Prediction) coder. VSELP belongs to a class of coders known as Code Excited Linear Predictive (CELP) coders. The coder analyzes a speech signal over a 20 msec segment and generates a 159 bit representation of it. The 159 bits specify 27 parameters employed in the VSELP speech coder. The total bit rate for the speech coding is thus 7950 bps. Because of the sensitivity of 77 of the parameter bits to channel errors, the speech coder data stream is appended with a 7 bit CRC and error protected with a rate 1/2 convolutional code. The error protection adds another 101 bits every 20 msec or 5050 bps to the total transmitted data rate. The data stream is diagonally interleaved with data from adjacent 20 msec speech segments over two time slots.

Three primary DSPs were available for application to the IS-54 speech coder specification at the time of issue of IS-54 Rev 0: the Motorola 56001, AT&T DSP16C, and TI TMS320C16 [9]. Due to the complexity and required processing speed of the speech codec DSP, power consumption is a significant concern. Power consumption for speech codec DSPs is approximately 500-600 mW although it is anticipated to drop to below 300 mW within the next 2 years.

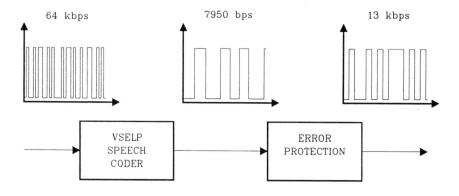

Figure 5.25 Speech Coder (DSP) Block Diagram

Channel Coding

Several stages of error correction and detection capability are used to perform channel coding. Both speech and control information are error protected to survive the rapid changing RF channel. The channel coder creates error protected signals by the use of convolutional coding, interleaving, CRC generation, and channel rate adjustment.

Convolutional coders provide error correction capability by adding redundant data bits. Convolutional coders are described by their rate where a relationship is formed by the number of bits entering and leaving the coder. Therefore, if we have a 1/2 rate convolutional coder, for every one bit that enters, two bits are generated. The larger the relationship, the more the redundancy and thus, the better the error protection ability. As a result, a 1/4 rate convolutional coder has much more error protection capability than a 1/2 rate coder. Speech and control data are protected by convolutional coding although for speech data, only certain bits are protected to minimize bandwidth requirements.

Data is interleaved between time slots to reduce susceptibility to burst errors inherent in the cellular radio system. Deep fades can corrupt many bits in one burst resulting in the entire slot being discarded. Interleaving distributes bits between adjacent slots so all the bits are not lost by one bad slot. Parity bits are appended to transmitted data to provide error detection capability. A CRC generator creates the parity bits by dividing input data bits by a polynomial formula and using the quotient (remainder bits) as the CRC parity bits. When the data has been acquired by the receiver assembly, the received data is divided by the same CRC polynomial formula and the resultant quotient is compared with the received quotient to determine if errors occur in the data.

After the data has been compressed and error protected, the data signals are then again compressed (in time only) into burst format. Burst timing offsets may be applied to allow for dynamic time alignment. Figure 5.26 displays how the data is compressed and time aligned to allow the data to be sent using 1/3 of the 48.6 kpbs channel.

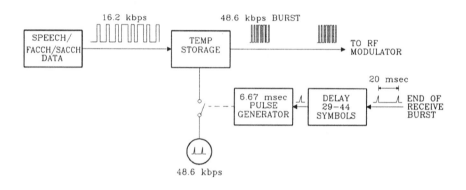

Figure 5.26 Data Compression and Time Alignment

Control Signal Multiplexing

Control signaling information must be multiplexed with the channel data. FACCH data messages replace speech data when rapid signaling commands are needed. SACCH messages are continuously multiplexed with the channel data as 12 bits per slot is dedicated for this out of band channel. Figure 5.27 shows how FACCH and SACCH messages are inserted into the channel data stream.

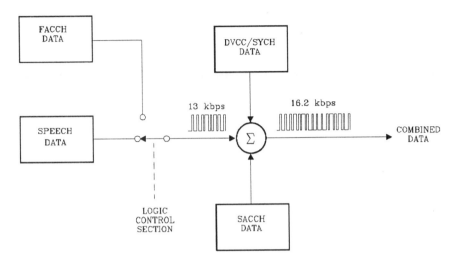

Figure 5.27 Control Signal Multiplexing

A new feature of the dual mode mobile station is Mobile Assisted Handoff (MAHO). The MS can be commanded by the BS to measure two types of channel quality. The MS can measure its received Bit Error Rate (BER) (see 5.5.1.5) and Received Signal Strength Indicator (RSSI) for up to 12 RF channels. This channel quality information is sent to the base station and is used to assist the handoff decision. Channel quality information is usually sent via the SACCH channel although channel quality information can be sent via the FACCH channel during DTX transmission.

5.5.1.3. Transmitter π/4 DQPSK Modulator and RF Amplifier

Combined rate adjusted data is finally applied to the DQPSK modulator and RF amplifier section. Each two bits entering the modulator will result in a relative phase change. The phase shifted RF signal is then amplified for transmission.

DQPSK Modulator

The DQPSK modulator converts binary data into a phase shifted RF carrier. Data sent to the modulator is grouped into two bits at a time where each two bits represents one symbol. Symbols are transmitted as relative phase changes rather than absolute phases.

For the balanced DQPSK modulator shown in figure 5.4, a reference oscillator provides two 90 degree phase shifted signals for the modulator. The serial data input is converted to two bit parallel data and supplied to the multipliers. Binary signals vary the amplitude of the phase shifted signals via the multipliers. Filters limit the impulse response (rapid transient) of the binary signals to ensure the RF carrier occupies the allocated bandwidth. The two amplitude varied signals are then summed together to form the phase shifted carrier signal.

The gross input bit rate to the modulator is 48.6 kbps, each 2 bits input results in a phase shift. Four phase shift quantities can exist and a phase shift is referred to as a symbol. Each symbol represents two bits (see table 5.3) which results in a symbol rate of 24.3 ksymbols/sec.

Table 5.3 Relative Phase Changes of $\pi/4$ DQPSK Modulation

Symbol		Bits	
degrees	radians	X_k	Y_k
+45	$+\pi/4$	0	0
+135	$+3\pi/4$	0	1
−135	$-3\pi/4$	1	1
−45	$-\pi/4$	1	0

RF Amplifier

The RF amplifier boosts the RF modulated signal to output levels specified by the base station (see figure 5.29). Unlike FM RF amplifiers, DQPSK RF amplifiers must have linear characteristics. Typically, to conserve power, class C push pull non-linear amplifiers are used as output amplifier stages for the Analog (FM) mobiles. If these were to be used for DQPSK amplification, non-linear performance would cause phase distortion which results in errors. Linear RF amplifiers are typically less efficient, approximately 30%, as opposed to near 50% for non-linear amplifiers. Because the duty cycle of the transmitter will be a maximum of 33% for a full rate mobile and 16.67% for a half rate, even with an increase in the peak power consumption requirement, a reduced average power consumption results. Significant work has been performed on linearizing (pre-distortion) class C amplifiers [10].

A new power class SCM (Station Class Mark) IV has been given to Dual Mode equipment which extends the dynamic range of the RF output power level. This means the variable attenuator must have an additional 12 dB range for portables.

While a duplexer is required for the Analog section, it is not necessarily required for the digital section. The transmitter and receiver do not operate simultaneously when on the digital channel. A simple PN switch may be enough to isolate the receiver from the transmitter allowing removal of the duplexer from the digital section (see figure 5.28). While DQPSK signals can pass through the duplexer, group delay will add some phase distortion [11] and power loss through the duplexer will require a higher rated power amplifier. By removing the duplexer, the power required from the RF amplifier is reduced adding extended battery life in transportables and portables.

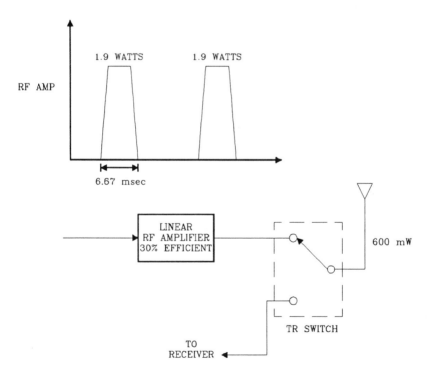

Figure 5.28 PN Switched RF Transceiver Section

5.5.1.4. Receiver RF Amplifier Section

The receiver RF amplifier section superheterodynes the RF frequency to a lower workable frequency range, demodulates the digital data, compensates (equalizes) to reduce the effects of RF phase and amplitude distortions, and provides signal quality information to be transmitted back to the base station. It consists of a low level RF amplifier, mixers, $\pi/4$ DQPSK demodulator, and equalizer (see figure 5.29).

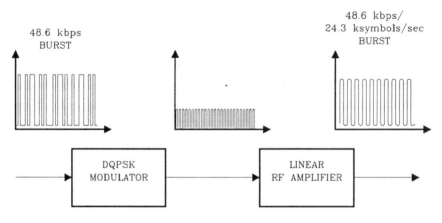

Figure 5.29 DQPSK Modulator & RF Amplifier

Receiver RF Amplifier

The receiver RF amplifier section selectively amplifies low level $\pi/4$ DQPSK signals. A sensitive receiver requires an RF amplifier so that the received signal that may be in the order of picowatts (–116 dBm) may be increased to the workable range of the mixer sections. The receiver amplifier is a broad band RF amplifier which has a variable gain controlled by the AGC. The AGC compensates for a large dynamic range of the received signal strength level which is approximately 70 dB. The AGC reduces the gain of the sensitive RF amplifier so as the input signal increases, no distortions due to overdriving the receiver occur.

A new requirement for Dual Mode mobiles is the ability to return signal quality information to the Base Station. This is in the form of RSSI (Received Signal Strength Indicator) and BER (Bit Error Rate) information. The accuracy requirements for the RSSI information are very strict and the mobile must be capable of measuring RSSI on any channel designated by the Base Station while a call is in progress.

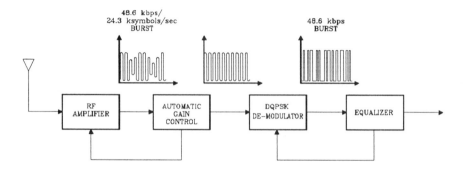

Figure 5.30 Receiver Amplifier Block Diagram

Mixer Sections

Because it is not cost effective to demodulate signals in the 800 MHz region directly, the incoming RF signal is mixed with another oscillator source to produce a lower Intermediate Frequency (IF). The oscillator source may be varied so the IF is a constant frequency simplifying IF amplifier design. Typically, a 2nd receiver mixer superheterodynes the first IF with another oscillator source to produce a much lower frequency than the first IF. The main advantage to this is a much lower IF frequency which permits narrow bandwidth filters to be used.

Demodulator

A $\pi/4$ DQPSK demodulator is used to extract digital data from the phase modulated signal. A local oscillator with a $90°$ phase shifted signal may be used to extract the quadrature information. The demodulator section determines which decision point the phase modulated signal has moved to. It then calculates the relative phase difference from the last decision point and determines the bits associated with that transition. In ideal conditions, decision points are exact locations. Unfortunately, severe distortions of the RF signal may require an equalizer.

Equalizer

Equalization compensates the demodulator section for phase and amplitude changes which occur on the RF channel. Two primary sources of these distortions are multipath signals and Doppler. Given a known bit stream input (synchronization word), it is possible to train the demodulator and adjust the decision points as channel quality changes.

Two classes of non-linear adaptive equalization architectures are being considered by many manufacturers for this type of application: The Decision Feedback Equalizer (DFE) [12] and the Maximum Likelihood Sequence Estimation (MLSE) [13]. Both of them can reduce the severe intersymbol interference caused by multipath signals, and at the same time operating with Doppler Shift of up to 80 Hz caused by the speed of the vehicle.

Multipath signals are a result of the same source RF signals being received at a different time due to different propagation paths. The Doppler effect is caused by the motion of the transmitter relative to the received signal. This results in the received frequency to vary in proportion to the speed of the vehicle. The doppler frequency can be calculated by the following formula:

$$f_d = f_c\,(u_v/c)$$

where:

f_c *is the carrier frequency*

f_d *is the doppler frequency*

u_v *is vehicle speed in meters/sec*

c is the speed of light (300 E^6 meters/sec)

While doppler effect is of little significance to Analog cellular, it has significant effect on digital phase transmission and equalizer operation.

5.5.1.5. Receiver Digital Signal Processing (DSP)

Demodulated data is error detected and corrected in the channel decoder, control data is demultiplexed, and speech data is expanded by the speech codec. Figure 5.31 shows the 16.2 kbps data from the receiver section is applied to DSP for demultiplexing and error correction.

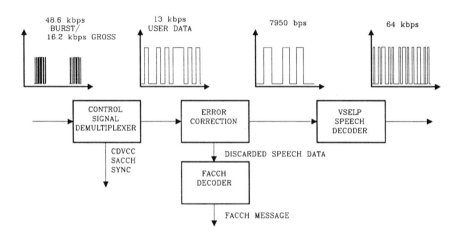

Figure 5.31 Speech Decoding (DSP) Block Diagram

Signal Demultiplexing

Speech, SACCH, FACCH, DVCC data signals from the demodulator are demultiplexed to separate signaling information. SACCH and DVCC data are simply demultiplexed by directing the dedicated bits from each burst to their control processing locations. Speech and FACCH demultiplexing is more challenging. Because FACCH data may replace speech data at any time, FACCH data is extracted by first attempting to decode and error correct speech data. If the CRC appears to be correct as decoded for a speech slot, the data is routed to the speech codec section. When the CRC is in error, the data is then decoded as a FACCH message. If the CRC appears to be correct, this FACCH data is routed to its call processing location.

Channel Decoder

The channel decoder de-interleaves, error corrects, and error detects speech, SACCH, FACCH and CDVCC data signals. Speech data is deinterleaved, error corrected, and applied to the speech decoder. SACCH and FACCH messages are deinterleaved, error corrected, and routed to the logic section for call processing. DVCC words are error detected, compared to the assigned DVCC to determine cochannel interference, and sent to the transmit section to be echoed back to the base station.

Error correction is made possible by the transmission of redundant information. A balance was maintained for error correction capability and channel bandwidth requirements. The more redundant bits that are transmitted, the larger the bandwidth that is required. Interleaving distributes one speech frame (20 msec for full rate) over two slot intervals and SACCH messages over 22 slots. If one slot of data is corrupted due to a deep fade, the bit errors are separated after deinterleaving. Correcting channel errors is more successful when the errors entering the channel decoder are distributed rather than occurring in bursts. The channel decoder also provides BER information back to the base station. This is used with the RSSI information to determine actual channel quality conditions received by the mobile which may better assist a handoff decision.

Speech Decoder

The speech decoder converts 7950 bps data to its original 64 kbps PCM form. Performance of the speech coder in poor radio conditions was shown to be superior to that of analog cellular. This is due to the error correction, interleaving, and error detection capability. Error correction provides resistance to random errors, interleaving reduces the effect of burst errors, and error detection permits the speech coder to discard uncorrected frames of information and to regenerate previous speech frame.

Because speech information is periodic for short term intervals, as frames are lost due to errors, the speech coder repeats previous speech information. Gradual muting takes place as the number of consecutive repeated frames increases. The end result is that for frames that could not be corrected, gaps are filled in.

The speech decoder will be bypassed when other user data is to be received from the network such as computer or facsimile data.

5.5.1.6. Receiver Audio Processing

Figure 5.32 shows how the receiver audio processing converts 64 kbps PCM speech data into audio signals. The 64 kbps PCM data is transformed back to an analog signal by a digital to analog converter. An audio filter is then used to minimize the step transients due to digital to analog converter. Many of the codec DSP chips have built in digital to analog convertors that perform this function.

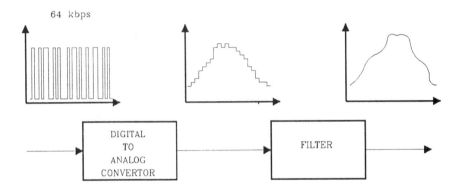

Figure 5.32 Receive Audio Processing Block Diagram

5.5.1.7. Logic Section

The Logic section uses programs stored in memory to operate the transceiver. Some memory is non-volatile to hold the stored programs for call processing, permanent information that cannot be changed, and semi-permanent information which rarely changes. Semi-permanent information includes the Number Assignment Module (NAM) which contains information about the unit's telephone number, class of service, and optional features. Permanent information includes information unique to a particular mobile that a user cannot change such as the Electronic Serial Number (ESN). Random access memory is also included to hold changing parameters as the mobile receives and initiates calls. A more detailed description and block diagram on the logic section can be found in 2.5.1.3.

In addition to the original call processing programs contained in the analog mobile, the mobile must be able to process digital messages and perform a new authentication algorithm. Although the message structure is completely different when operating on a digital channel, the call processing remains relatively unchanged. This results in only a moderate increase in call processing software requirements. However, a new processing procedure has been developed to reduce fraudulent use. This encryption algorithm uses new stored data and random data received in the overhead information message stream to encrypt the ESN prior to accessing the system (see 5.6).

5.5.2. Antenna Assembly

Displayed in figure 5.23 (dual mode mobile block diagram) shows a duplexer used as the RF signal combiner. Figure 5.28 (PN switch) shows an alternate method to combine receive and transmit signals when on a digital traffic channel. The digital cellular structure was designed to allow the mobile, once on the digital channel, not to require a duplexer (two band pass filters). Because Dual Mode mobiles are required to operate in either Analog or Digital mode, all Dual Mode mobiles will have a duplexer. This leads to the question: what happens to the duplexer when the mobile is in the digital mode? The result is two implementation methods for the digital transceiver: a duplexer method and a TR switch method.

5.5.3. Control Head

The control head consists of a display, keypad, audio interface, and interconnect cabling. The control head is the interface between the user and the cellular system. The operation of a dual mode and analog only transceiver need not be different, although some of the new features such as short message transmission and calling number identification may lead to different types of operation and displays.

A display readout is usually provided which indicates user entered digits and calling number identification. The display may also provide the user with status information such as Digital Channel, NO SERVICE, ROAM, IN USE, LOCK, and HORN ALERT (optional). A keypad or voice recognition device allows the user to enter information to control the phone. The audio interface typically consists of a speaker and microphone mounted in a handset. Hands free operation is usually provided to allow the use of microphone and speaker assemblies mounted in automobiles. Because of the delays digital signal processing introduces in speech transmission, the echos generated by the hands free circuit can be particularly annoying. Special echo cancelling circuitry must be included to reduce echos when in the hands free mode.

5.6. AUTHENTICATION

Authentication is a process of validating a mobile subscriber where information is exchanged between the system and the mobile to determine if the user is a valid customer of the system. The IS-54 Rev B standard has this new validation and confidentiality capability which reduces cellular fraud and enhances voice privacy.

The authentication process includes new features such as a PIN (personal identification number), SSD (shared secret data), a received random number, and a CAVE algorithm which are used to encrypt the ESN. A PIN is combined with a previously stored A_ key to create shared secret data and a new A_key. A random number (RAND) is continuously sent in the overhead message train which is stored in the mobile station. This secret data and the random number is provided to the CAVE algorithm to encrypt the ESN prior to transmission. Figure 5.33 shows how access using the authentication procedure is performed.

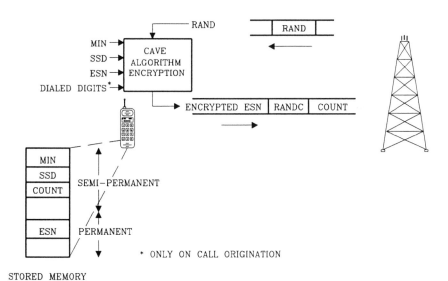

Figure 5.33 Authentication Procedure for Dual Mode Mobiles

5.7. SUMMARY

A dual mode mobile station must conform to IS-54 and IS-55 industry standards to ensure compatibility with the cellular system. Key system parameters include channel frequency assignment, power output, modulation type, time slot, and RF channel structure. The frequency allocation remains 824 MHz to 849 MHz for mobile station transmit and 869 MHz to 894 MHz for mobile station receive. All channels are frequency duplex separated by 45 MHz. Some RF channels may be converted to a TDMA channel structure which permits Time Division Duplex (TDD) operation which use $\pi/4$ DQPSK modulation to communicate with the cellular system.

$\pi/4$ DQPSK modulation was chosen for its bandwidth efficiency. A balanced modulator may be used to create a $\pi/4$ DQPSK signal by amplitude modulating and combining two 90° phase shifted signals. An I-Q pattern may be used to view the amplitude and phase relationships between the two 90° phase shifted signals. Binary information input to the modulator results in the shifting of phase. A starting or ending point phase and amplitude is referred to as a decision point.

Three types of slot structures exist: a forward slot, a reverse slot, and a shortened burst slot. The forward slot transfers speech and control information from the base station to the mobile. The reverse slot transfers speech and control information from the mobile to the base station. The shortened burst is transmitted by the mobile when it begins operating in a large cell area where it is necessary to determine time alignment information. Dynamic time alignment adjusts the relative transmit start time to compensate for propagation delays.

Control channel signaling remains the same although some voice channels may be converted to secondary dedicated control channels. When combined paging and access channels are used on the primary dedicated control channels, the dual mode mobile will listen for pages on its access channel and attempt access on the paging channels. The analog voice channels remain the same with an addition of parameters necessary for handoff to a digital channel. Although the digital traffic channel signaling is entirely different, the messages transferred have a similar functionality to the analog voice channel. A DVCC word is transponded back to the base station which is similar to SAT. Two types of control message transfer are allowed on the digital traffic channel, FACCH and SACCH. FACCH messages replace speech with control information. SACCH messages are sent by dedicated bits allocated during each burst which allows the sending of messages without interruption of speech.

Mobile operation can be divided into four modes: initialization, idle, access, and conversation. When a mobile station is first turned on, it performs the initialization mode by tuning to the strongest control channel and extracting system overhead information. It then remains in the idle mode where it continues to update system information and waits for a call to be originated or received. When access to the system is required, the mobile performs an authentication procedure and attempts access by sending a message indicating what type of access is required. Conversation mode is performed on either an analog voice channel or digital traffic channel where voice and data information may be transferred.

The Analog Mobile Station consists of three sections: a transceiver section, antenna section, and control head. The transceiver converts audio to RF and RF to audio. The antenna assembly transforms energy to and from free space propagation. A control head allows the operator to command the mobile station. The dual mode transceiver section consists of an analog (FM) transceiver and digital (π/4 DQPSK) transceiver contained in one assembly. The control head and antenna assemblies need not change for a dual mode mobile.

References:

[1] Electronic Industries Association, EIA Interim Standard IS-54, Dual-Mode Mobile Station - Base Station Compatibility Standard, (February 1990).

[2] EIA/TIA, IS-55, "Recommended Minimum Performance Standards for 800 MHz Dual Mode Mobile Stations," (July 1991).

[3] Electronic Industries Association, EIA-553, "Mobile Station - Land Station Compatibility Specification," (1990).

[4] Electronic Industries Association, EIA Interim Standard IS-19-B, Recommended Minimum Standards for 800 MHz Cellular Subscriber Units, (May 1988).

[5] Ferrel G. Stremler, *Introduction to Communication Systems*, (1982: 2nd edition, Addison-Wesley), pp. 302-304.

[6] Telecommunications Industries Association, Washington D.C., "Digital Traffic Channel Features to be Incorporated into the Analog Voice Channel," TR45.3.2.4/91.05.06.02, May 6, 1991, Audiovox Corporation.

[7] Electronic Industries Association, EIA-553, "Mobile Station - Land Station Compatibility Specification," (1990), pp. 2-24.

[8] Telecommunications Industry Association, "DTMF Tone Processing Via the Decoder," TR45.3.2/90.07.26.10, Motorola Corporation, June 1990.

[9] EETIMES, Bindra, Ashok, Issue 598, July 9, 1990.

[10] Michael Faulkner, "Adaptive Linearisation Using Pre-distortion," IEEE 1990 Vehicular Technology Conference, pp. 35-40.

[11] Donald G. Fink, Donald Christiansen, *Electronic Engineers Handbook*, (2nd edition, McGraw-Hill, 1982), pp.12-29, 30.

[12] P. Monsen: "Feedback Equalization For Fading Dispersive Channels," IEEE Trans Inform. Theory, (Jan 1971), vol. IT-17, pp. 55-64.

[13] G. Ungerboeck: "Adaptive Maximum Receiver For Carrier-Modulated Data Transmission Systems," IEEE Trans. Comm., (May 1974), vol. COM-22, pp. 624-636.

Chapter 6

Dual Mode Cellular System Network

6.1. INTRODUCTION

The dual mode cellular system network is composed of Base Stations, a Mobile Switching Center (MSC)[1], communication links, and PSTN interconnection. A dual mode network differs from its analog predecessor by having both analog and digital transmission capability, new features, and advanced access authentication. Additionally, the dual mode infrastructure has some cost effective advantages over the analog system. This chapter describes these basic dual mode network elements, their technical characteristics, operation, and new dual mode cellular system planning considerations. Descriptions in this chapter are used with reference to chapter 3 to cover the Analog cellular network part of the Dual Mode equipment.

6.2. DUAL MODE BASE STATION

A dual mode Base Station provides multiple-channel and multiple-type transmitting and receiving facilities for a cell site area. To provide a standard RF communications link between the Base Station and Mobile Stations, Base Stations must operate within electrical parameters, conform to signaling structures, and call process signaling messages. The dual mode Base Station contains functional sections to comply with these requirements.

6.2.1. Base Station Parameters

Dual Mode Base Stations must operate in conformance with IS-54 [1] and IS-56 [2] to ensure interoperability with Mobile Stations. These standards contain the specific parameters for the RF channel frequency assignment, power output, modulation, and channel structure.

---

1   The common term MTSO (Mobile Telephone Switching Office) has been replaced by MSC (Mobile Switching Center).

6.2.1.1. Channel Frequency Assignment

The 25 MHz x 2 cellular frequency allocation remains the same where the base station transmit band is 869-894 MHz and the receiver band is 824-849 MHz (see figure 5.1). All RF channels are frequency duplex (separated by 45 MHz) although digital channels divide receive and transmit frequencies into time slots which allow TDD (Time Division Duplex) operation. Analog and digital RF channels occupy a maximum of 30 kHz bandwidth.

To allow the overlay of a separate digital system on an existing analog system, and to increase control channel capacity, some of the analog voice channels may be converted to control channels. These control channels are optional and are an implementation issue (see 6.6.3).

6.2.1.2. Base Station RF Power Output

The maximum Effective Radiated Power (ERP) for base station digital channels had not changed from its analog predecessor. For a more detailed description of the maximum RF output power, see section 3.2.1.2.

6.2.1.3. Modulation

Base Station transceivers must be capable of the same FSK and FM modulation as the analog system and must also have $\pi/4$ DQPSK modulation capability. Control channels continue to use FSK modulation. Analog voice channels use both FM and FSK modulation. Digital traffic channels use $\pi/4$ DQPSK modulation. A description of $\pi/4$ DQPSK modulation can be found in 5.2.3.

6.2.1.4. Channel Structure

There are three types of channels for a dual mode cellular system: dedicated control channels, analog (FM) voice channels, and digital traffic channels. Dedicated control channels provide system parameter information and perform channel assignment. Analog voice and digital traffic channels allow the user to transport information (usually voice) through to the MSC. An omni- directional dual mode Base Station will have one primary dedicated control channel, an optional secondary control channel, and several analog voice and digital traffic channels. The dual mode control channels and analog voice channels perform all of the analog cellular functions as defined in EIA-553 (see 2.3.1 and 2.3.2). A detailed description of the digital traffic channel structure can be found in 5.2.4.

6.2.2. Base Station Operation

The Base Station transmits and receives RF signals from Mobile Stations within its particular service area, converts the RF signals to voice and data information, and transfers this information between the base station and MSC via communication links. A description of Base Station signaling, call processing, maintenance, and diagnostics can be found in 3.2.2. A significant difference in dual mode base station operation is the ability to RF monitor channel quality via the MS (see 5.5.1.2).

6.2.3. Dual Mode Base Station Detailed Description

The dual mode Base Station consists of a control section, analog and digital transceivers, RF amplifiers, receiver multicoupler, RF combiner, communication processors, scanning receiver, power supplies, and an antenna assembly.

A control section coordinates the overall operation of the Base Station. The transceiver sections are similar to the dual mode Mobile Station transceiver sections as they convert audio to RF signals and RF to audio signals. RF amplifiers boost the output of the transceivers so enough RF energy can cover the designated cell site area. Receiver multicouplers split the received RF signals to allow connection to all of its associated Base Station receivers. The RF combiner allows the merging of radio channels from a multiple of transceivers to one antenna assembly. Communications processors translate audio and control information between the BS and MSC. The scanning receiver provides the capability of measuring the signal strength on any of the cellular channels.[2] The power supply provides operating voltages and backup systems to maintain operation when primary power is interrupted. Many of the sections within the Base Station will be duplicated in the event of equipment failure. Figure 6.1 shows a dual mode Base Station block diagram.

---

2   The scanning receiver may not measure the signal strength on digital traffic channels if
     the MSC relies on the channel quality measurements returned by the mobile station.

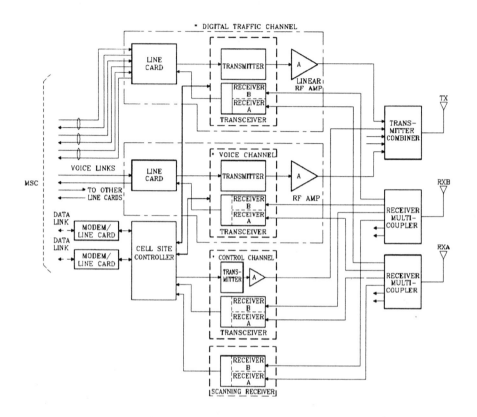

Figure 6.1 Dual Mode Base Station Block Diagram

6.2.3.1. Controller

The controller coordinates the operation of the BS equipments based on commands received from the MSC and its own stored program control. The controller consists of stored program memory, microprocessor, and interface circuitry which allows control of BS equipments. The controller call processes messages, commands analog voice, digital traffic, and control channel transceivers, and provides for maintenance and diagnostic functions.

6.2.3.2. Transceivers

The Base Station transceiver sections have similar transmitter, receiver, and logic processing sections as the dual mode Mobile Station (see 5.5). A Base Station transmitter has audio processing, analog and digital modulation, and an RF power amplifier. The receiver frequently has diversity reception which requires dual RF amplifiers, demodulator, and audio processing sections. The logic section of the Base Station transceiver consists of control signal routing which inserts and extracts audio and digital signaling messages from the radio channel. Unlike the Mobile Station, these sections may be physically separate and located with other transceiver sections of the similar type. For example, a single equipment rack may contain all of the RF amplifiers.

6.2.3.3. RF Power Amplifier

A power amplifier unit is provided for each transceiver to increase its transmitter output power. For the FM transceivers, a class C RF amplifier may be used for high efficiency as FM modulation does not require linear amplification. For the $\pi/4$ DQPSK transceivers, a linear amplifier must be used.

6.2.3.4. RF Multicoupler

A receiver multicoupler is provided for each receive antenna to allow a single antenna to serve several receivers. There is no required change for the RF Multicoupler section to support a digital traffic channel [3]. See 3.2.3.4. for a more detailed description of the RF multicoupler section.

6.2.3.5. RF Combiner

The RF combiner is similar to the duplexer where an antenna is shared between several devices operating on different frequencies. There is no required change for the RF combiner section to support a digital traffic channel [4]. See 3.2.3.5. for a more detailed description of the RF combiner section.

6.2.3.6. Communications Link Processor

The Base Station must be capable of interfacing to a communications link for the transfer of voice and data information to the MSC. Communication links transfer information by landline, fiber, or microwave. The function of the communications link processor is to convert the audio (baseband) signals between the Base Station equipments to a format suitable for transfer via communication links.

The most significant changes between analog and digital communications link processing is the adapting of digital baseband signals to match the communications link. Due to the extreme low rate of speech codec information, 7950 bps for full rate and approximately 4000 bps for half rate, it is possible to sub rate multiplex several users on one 64 kbps DS0 link. 6.6.5 discusses several implementations that allow subrate multiplexing.

6.2.3.7. Antenna Assembly

The antenna assembly transforms RF energy between the transceivers into electromagnetic waves propagating in free space. There is no required change for the antenna section to support a digital traffic channel [5]. See 3.2.3.7. for a detailed description of the antenna assembly.

6.2.3.8. Scanning Receiver

A scanning receiver is used to measure the mobile's signal strength for potential handoff channels. The new dual mode MAHO capability reduces the need for a scanning receiver. Because channel quality can be returned from the mobile station on any channel (see 5.5.1.2), it is possible to command the MS to measure the signal strength of potential handoff channels (analog or digital). This signal quality information returned from the mobile station can be used to determine handoff requirements.

6.2.3.9. Power Supplies

Primary power for cell sites is usually commercial AC power supplied by the local utility company. AC power is converted to regulated and filtered AC and DC voltage levels required by the equipments. In the event of a loss of primary power, backup supplies are provided to maintain operation. Backup energy sources may include batteries and a generator.

While the linear RF amplifiers consume approximately 60% more power than the class C amplifiers, the overall system efficiency for TDMA digital cellular is greater due to the multiplexing of three channels on one RF amplifier. This results in a reduced total power consumption for base station RF amplifiers. This system efficiency will double with the introduction of half rate codecs and double again with the use of DSI (digital speech interpolation). This further reduces the backup power supply and cooling system requirements.

6.3. MOBILE SWITCHING CENTER

An MSC coordinates all of the base stations within its network, routes signals to and from the PSTN, and provides administrative and maintenance functions. The MSC has no required standards and its implementation is often proprietary. The mobile switching center is similar to a land line switching center. An MSC has the ability to switch the mobile to either the land line telephone network, another mobile, or private lines.

Changes to convert an MSC to dual mode capability are implementation specific and may range from a simple software change to installing complex DSP (Digital Signal Processors) equipment [6]. See 3.3.3. for a detailed description of the equipments contained in the MTSO which are the same for a MSC.

6.4. PSTN INTERCONNECTION

The MSC is the gateway from the cellular system to the land line (PSTN) telephone network. The only required change for the PSTN interconnection to support a digital traffic channel is the addition of an echo canceller to overcome the effect of delays due to digital speech processing [7]. For a more detailed description of the PSTN interconnection, see 3.5.

6.5. NETWORK OPERATION

An MS may by assigned to an analog voice channel or digital traffic channel on call origination, termination, or handoff. The dual mode MS has been given the capability to request a change between a digital traffic channel and an analog voice channel. A new access authentication procedure has been added which requires both intrasystem and intersystem network operation. The following descriptions provide a perspective on possible network operations for digital channel assignment. The assignment of analog channels is described in 3.6 with the exception of added authentication processing (see 5.6). While some implementations may allow for different intersystem signaling, the functional operations are the same.

6.5.1. Land to Mobile Digital Channel Call

A landline user calls a Mobile Station (see figure 6.2) by dialing the MS telephone number. The call is routed through the PSTN to the MSC. The MSC then commands all the Base Stations in its system to page the MS. If the MS is active in the system, it responds to the page by locking onto the strongest control channel and attempting access and indicating the access is a result of a page message. An authentication procedure is performed by the mobile station to encrypt the ESN by using the latest received RAND and other stored parameters. Authorized access is verified by comparing the received MS encrypted ESN to stored information in the MSC subscriber database. The Base Station then assigns the MS to a digital traffic channel via an ITCD (Initial Traffic Channel Designation) message. The MS tunes to the assigned digital traffic channel, receives the assigned DVCC, and begins to transmit DVCC words to the base station via shortened bursts (see figure 5.10). After the BS has received the correct DVCC on the digital traffic channel, the BS sends a time alignment message. When the MS has time aligned, the MS returns a complete burst with a time alignment acknowledgement. The base station then sends an alert (ring) message. When the receipt of the alert message is acknowledged by the MS, it is relayed back to the PSTN to allow the landline party to hear a ringing signal. When the MS operator answers the ringing signal (usually by pressing SND), the MS sends a connect message. This confirms to the MSC that the MS operator has answered the call. The call is then connected and conversation begins.

If the landline party hangs up, a command is sent from the MSC to the MS to disconnect. The mobile station then sends an acknowledgement message and transmission is ended. If the MS goes on-hook (by pressing the END key), the MS transmits a disconnect message, receives an acknowledge from the base, and terminates transmission.

6.5.2. Mobile Digital Call to Landline

A Mobile Station calls a landline party (see figure 6.3) by dialing the landline telephone number and pressing the SEND key. The MS then scans and locks onto the strongest control channel and attempts access by sending

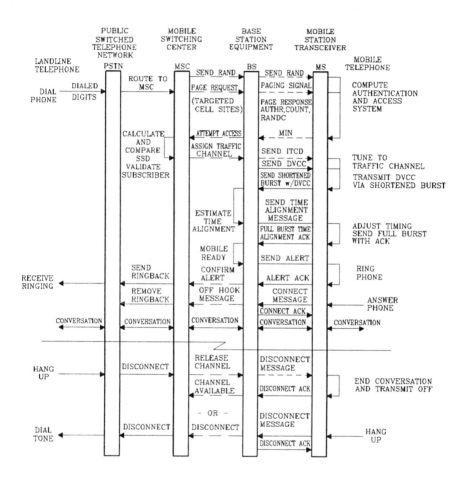

Figure 6.2 Land to Mobile Digital Call Processing

the dialed digits and indicating the access is a result of an origination request (see 2.4.3). The mobile station performs encryption of the ESN information with the latest RAND parameter and dialed digits. Authorized access is verified by comparing the received MS encrypted information to stored information in the MSC subscriber database. If access is successful, the Base Station assigns the MS to a digital traffic channel via an ITCD (Initial Traffic Channel Designation) message. The MS tunes to the assigned digital traffic channel, receives the assigned DVCC, and transmits the DVCC words via shortened bursts. After the BS has received the correct DVCC on the digital traffic channel, the BS sends a time alignment message. When the MS has time aligned, the MS returns a complete burst with a time alignment acknowledgement. The base station then indicates the MS is ready and the MSC sends the dialed digits to the PSTN. The PSTN then rings the landline party and returns a status tone (ring/busy) to the MSC. The MSC then commands the MS to connect so the MS operator can hear the ring/busy signal. When the landline party answers the call, the PSTN completes the connection and conversation begins.

If the landline party hangs up, a command is sent from the MSC to the MS to disconnect, the mobile sends an acknowledgement message, and transmission is ended. If the MS goes on-hook (by pressing the END key), the MS transmits a disconnect message, receives an acknowledge from the base, and terminates transmission.

6.5.3. Mobile Digital to Mobile Digital Call

The process for completing MS to MS calls is similar to those described for MS calls to and from landline users except the calls between the mobile units that are served by the same MSC do not need to be routed through the PSTN.

6.5.4. Handoff

As an MS moves out of its serving cell site area while a call is in progress, its received signal quality decreases. Figure 6.4 shows when the signal quality falls below a predetermined level, adjacent Base Station equipments are instructed to measure the signal strength of the MS. Handoff may occur from analog to analog traffic channels (discussed in 3.6.4), from analog to digital traffic channels, from digital to analog traffic channels, or from digital to digital traffic channels. The Base Station with the highest signal quality is selected as the handoff cell site. The selected BS begins to transmit on a new channel and the MS is commanded from the serving cell site to tune to the new voice channel.

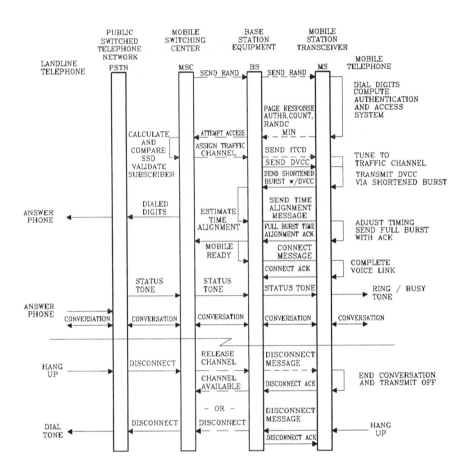

Figure 6.3 Mobile Digital to Landline Call Processing

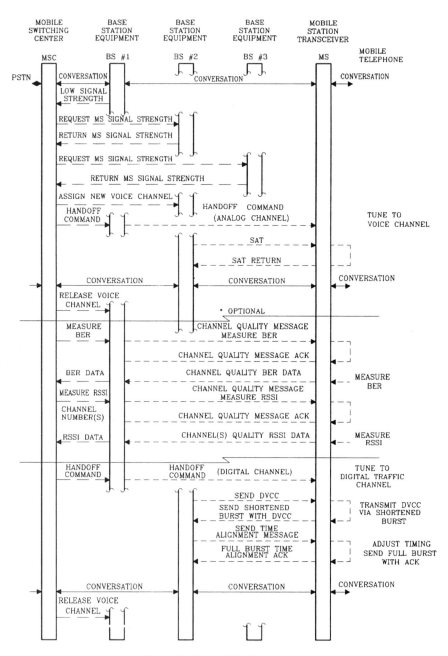

Figure 6.4 Handoff Call Processing

For the digital to analog channel handoff, the selected BS begins to transmit on a new channel and the MS is commanded from the serving cell site to tune to the new analog voice channel. When the MS successfully transponds the new SAT tone back to the BS, the MSC switches the communications circuit to the new serving Base Station and conversation continues.

For dual mode transceivers operating on a digital traffic channel, channel quality information can be requested from the mobile station by the base station. This information can be used to help determine when and where a handoff signal is necessary. The BS may request BER information from the channel the MS is currently operating on. When the channel quality falls below an acceptable level, a handoff may be necessary and the BS may request the MS to measure the signal strength of up to 12 different channels (analog or digital). These channels typically are control channels of adjacent cell sites. The Base Station with the highest signal quality is selected as the handoff cell site.

An analog channel to digital channel handoff is more complex as it involves assigning a channel, time slot, DVCC, channel codec parameters, and establishing time alignment if required. The MS must tune to the correct digital traffic channel, operate on a particular time slot, transpond DVCC, determine which codec (future option) to use, and transmit shortened bursts if necessary. In large cells, shortened bursts may be required until time alignment can be established.

A digital channel to digital channel handoff is essentially the same as an analog channel to digital channel handoff with the exception that the channel assignment information is transferred on the digital traffic channel.

6.5.5. Change of Preferred Mode

The MS may autonomously request to be transferred to a different type of channel. The primary reason for this capability is that facsimile and modem data cannot be sent via the codec on the digital traffic channel. To send complex audio information (non-voice), the MS may request to be handed off from a digital traffic channel to an analog voice channel.

6.5.6. Authentication

To prevent fraudulent use of a MS, some of the access request information (MIN/ESN) is encrypted using Shared Secret Data and other parameters (see 5.6). The encrypted ESN (AUTHR) and other parameters are transferred via the RF channel to the base station. The base station uses the same parameters to produce an encrypted ESN. This AUTHRbase should be the same as the AUTHRmobile. If not, the call may be disconnected [8].

Authenticating an MS in a visited system requires intersystem signaling and passing of a limited amount of user specific data. Because the database in the visited system does not contain all of the parameters necessary to create the AUTHRbase, when the first access request is received from a visiting mobile station, user specific information is requested from the mobile's home system. The portion of the users Shared Secret Data (SSD) is returned to the visiting system so creation of the AUTHRbase can be performed. This SSD information is maintained at the visited system so future access requests do not require signaling back to the home system for each access request [9]. Figure 6.5 shows the intersystem signaling requirements to send user secret data between the home system and visited system.

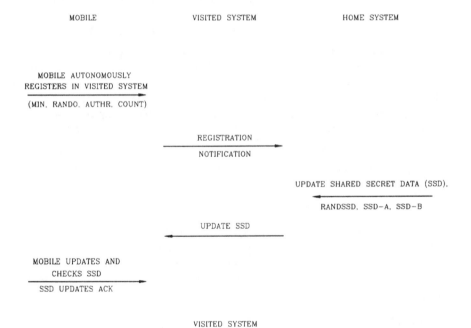

Figure 6.5 Authentication Intersystem Signaling

6.5.7. Change of Privacy Mode

While operating on a digital traffic channel, the user may request a privacy mode if supported by the network. The digital speech data will be encrypted when operating in voice privacy mode so another user cannot successfully decode the conversation without a known encryption key. The encryption key changes on a per call basis. A unique portion of the SSD is used to encrypt the voice data. Since this SSD is passed to the visiting system during access, this allows for voice data encryption in a visited system if that visited system has voice encryption capability.

6.6. DESIGN CONSIDERATIONS FOR A DUAL MODE CELLULAR NETWORK

Chapter 3 discussed the design of a cellular system. While this process is also used for a dual mode cellular system, additional considerations include delay spread, use of repeaters, control channel configuration, integrated and overlay networks, and intrasystem communications configurations.

6.6.1. Delay Spread

Considerable discussions have occurred and extensive requirements have been placed on transceiver equipment to include equalizers for combatting delay spread. Delay spread results when signals are reflected off distant objects and are received at a later time than the direct signal between the mobile and base stations. This results in phase and amplitude distortions of the original signal [10]. While errors caused by delay spread can be minimized by equalizers, system design can also influence delay spread received by the mobile unit. Figure 6.6 shows multipath propagation in a mountainous area. In figure a, one high power transmitter introduces excessive delay spread to the mobile unit. In figure b, several low power transmitters are used which limit multipath propagation. As cellular systems mature, cell site areas will be reduced and delay spread conditions will also be improved.

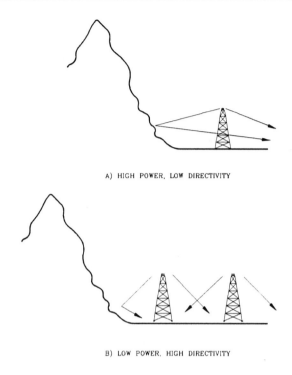

A) HIGH POWER, LOW DIRECTIVITY

B) LOW POWER, HIGH DIRECTIVITY

Figure 6.6 Delay Spread Consideration

6.6.2. Repeaters

The use of repeaters will play a vital part in bringing cost effective cellular service to rural areas. It is possible to extend the range of analog and digital channels by the use of repeaters. While it is possible to extend the range over a hundred miles, this increased range will introduce propagation delays and phase distortion. The propagation delay introduced by repeater amplifiers may exceed the maximum delay offset the mobile units are capable of when operating on a digital traffic channel. In addition, repeaters may use class C amplifiers that introduce phase distortion which may result in high BERs when assigned to a digital traffic channel.

6.6.3. Control Channel Configuration

Significant concern exists on the ability of the control channels to handle the additional calling capacity of the digital system. To increase control channel capacity, the paging and access functions can be performed on two separate channels. For an analog only system, when the paging and access channels are divided, no significant capacity gain results. The paging channel only uses its forward channel to pass global system and page messages to the mobile. No transmission occurs on the reverse channel of the paging channel. For the access channel, the mobile transmits on the reverse channel and only system information is transmitted on the forward channel.

To optimize the capacity resources of the control channels, the dual mode mobile reverses the access and paging channels when separate paging and access channels are used on the primary dedicated control channels. With an equal number of Analog and Dual Mode mobiles, this should effectively double the paging capacity. The capacity usage as shown in figure 6.7 displays what proportions of message data is transferred on the forward and reverse channels using this method.

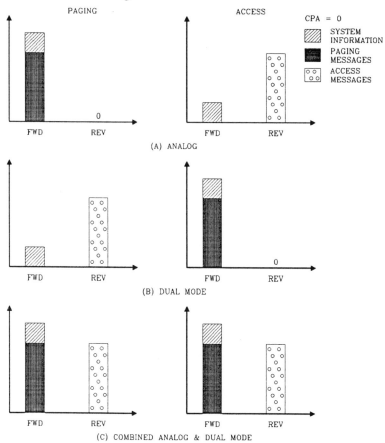

Figure 6.7 Control Channel Capacity Usage

6.6.4. Integrated and Overlay Systems

The dual mode cellular system supports two methods of implementation. First is an integrated approach where one controller is responsible for both Analog and Digital channels. The second approach is the overlay (side by side operation) of an Analog and Dual Mode switch. The integrated system uses the same control channel to assign both analog and digital traffic channels. This requires the same MSC to control the analog and digital channels. Figure 6.8 shows a block diagram of an integrated system.

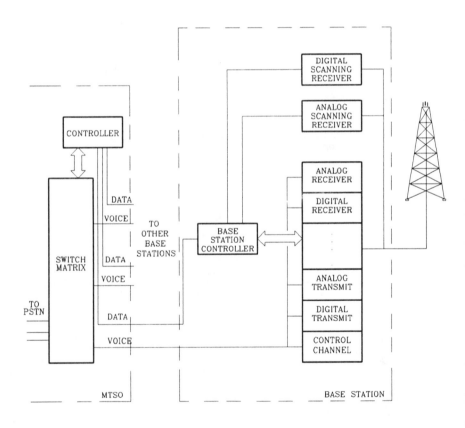

Figure 6.8 Integrated Dual Mode Cellular System Block Diagram

The overlay system uses different control channels to assign analog voice and digital traffic channels. This results in the removal of voice channel spectrum for additional dedicated control channels. A benefit of the overlay system is two vendors can supply equipment, two switches and two controllers could exist side by side allowing a rapid transition to digital capability. Figure 6.9 shows a block diagram of an overlay system.

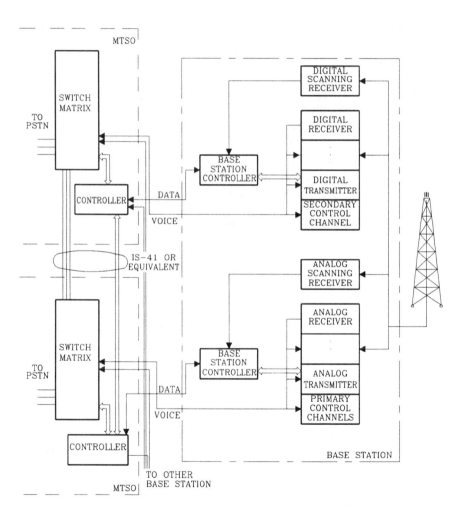

Figure 6.9 Overlay Dual Mode System Block Diagram

6.6.5. Intrasystem Configurations

Whatever the transmission medium of choice between the cell site and MTSO, a cost is involved with maintaining the data and voice links. The efficiency between these points can be optimized by various methods such as subrate multiplexing. Equipment configuration options include locating the channel coder and speech codec at the base station, placing the speech codec and channel coder at the MSC, and installing the channel coder at the base station and speech coder at the MSC.

6.6.5.1. Channel Coder and Codec Location at Base Station

Figure 6.10 shows that by placing the channel coder and speech codec at the cell site, 64 kbps voice data is available in DS0 formation and may be easily inserted into the system. The result is a simplistic implementation at the expense of efficiency between the cell site and switching center. The efficiency can be improved by data compression techniques such as ADPCM (see 3.4).

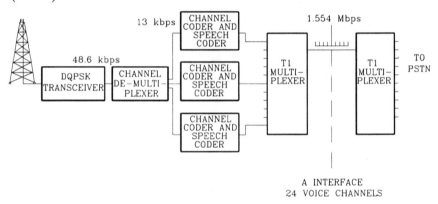

Figure 6.10 System Block Diagram with Codec and Coder at the Base Station.

6.6.5.2. Channel Coder and Codec at MSC

Figure 6.11 shows a configuration which extracts the raw channel data rate of 48.6 kbps and places it directly on one DS0 by subrate multiplexing. The base station then has an efficiency of 3 traffic channels per DS0. The primary advantages of this configuration are the ability to service and support equipment in one location, reduce base station size and complexity, and reduce the number of redundant equipment.

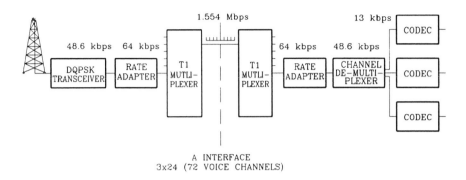

Figure 6.11 System Block Diagram with the Channel Decoder and Codec at the MSC

6.6.5.3. Channel Coder at BS and Codec at MSC

Figure 6.12 shows the most efficient configuration where eight voice channels can be subrate multiplexed on one DS0 link for a full rate speech coder. This will increase to 16 users on one DS0 when half rate codecs are introduced. The channel coder de-interleaves the data and performs convolutional decoding resulting in voice data rate at the original data of 7950 bps per traffic channel. This data is submultiplexed with up to 8 users for insertion into one DS0.

6.6.6. System Expansion

In 1988, the CTIA specified capacity improvements which required an evolution of technology [11]. The IS-54 standard provides for this evolution of technology by allowing for a Half Rate Codec which multiplexes 6 users on one RF channel. Because technology innovations and speech codec processing requirements are extensive, work is progressing slowly on low bit rate codecs. Introduction of DSI (Digital Speech Interpolation) can be expected within the next few years that may allow approximately 11 to 17 users to share one RF channel [12]. Use of DSI can be easily implemented when several RF channels have been converted to the IS-54 TDMA channel structure.

Both the half rate speech coder and DSI allow for a gradual technology evolution that will meet the needs of the industry as specified in the UPR.

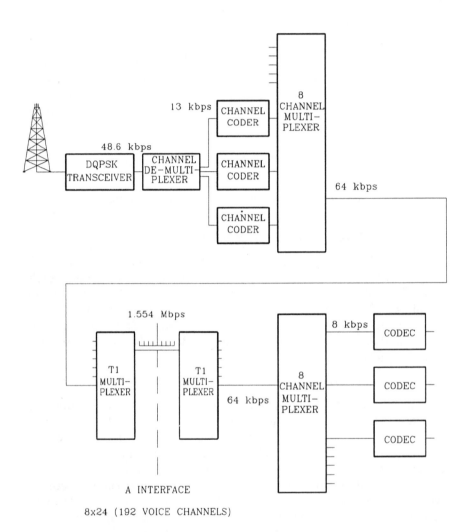

Figure 6.12 System Block Diagram with the Codec at the MSC and the Channel Coder at the Base Station.

6.7. SUMMARY

A dual mode cellular system network consists of Base Stations (BS), a Mobile Switching Center (MSC), communication links, and PSTN interconnections.

Base stations have multiple type transceivers that convert RF signals to and from mobile stations for transfer to and from the MSC. Each base station performs call processing, maintenance, and diagnostic functions. Dual mode base stations consist of a control section, analog and digital transceivers, RF amplifiers, receiver multicouplers, RF combiner, communications processors, scanning receiver, power supplies, and an antenna assembly. The primary difference between the dual mode base station and analog base station is the ability to transfer voice and data information on a digital traffic channel.

An MSC coordinates the base stations within its network and routes signals to and from the PSTN. The MSC consists of controllers, switching assembly, communications processors, operator terminal, subscriber database, and backup energy sources. Changes to the MSC are implementation specific and may range from a simple software change to installing complex DSPs.

The network operation must allow mobile station assignment to an analog voice channel or digital traffic channel on call origination, termination, mobile preferred mode request, or handoff. A new access authentication procedure has been added which requires both intrasystem and intersystem network operation.

Considerations unique to designing a dual mode cellular system include delay spread, use of repeaters, control channel configuration, integrated vs. overlay systems, intrasystem communication configurations, increased co-channel rejection, and system expansion options.

References:

[1] Electronic Industries Association, EIA Interim Standard IS-54, Rev B, "Dual-Mode Mobile Station - Base Station Compatibility Standard," (November 1990).

[2] EIA/TIA, IS-56, "Recommended Minimum Performance Standards for 800 MHz Base Stations Supporting Dual Mode Mobile Stations," (August 1991).

[3] Telecommunications Industries Association Transition to Digital Symposium, "Transition and Compatibility," TIA, Orlando, FL, (Sept. 1991).

[4] *Ibid.*

[5] *Ibid.*

[6] *Ibid.*

[7] *Ibid.*

[8] CTIA Fraud Subcommittee Meeting: *Authentication & User Interface*, Dallas, Texas, (August 21, 1991).

[9] Telecommunications Industries Association Transition to Digital Symposium, "Authentication and Voice Privacy," TIA, Orlando, FL, (Sept. 1991).

[10] William Lee, *Mobile Cellular Telecommunications Systems*, (McGraw Hill, 1989), p. 22.

[11] CTIA, Users' Performance Requirements, Issue 1, September 8, 1988.

[12] Telecommunications Industries Association Transition to Digital Symposium, "Digital Speech Coding," TIA, Orlando, FL, (Sept. 1991).

Chapter 7

Cellular System Economics

This chapter describes cost factors that relate to how Dual Mode conversion may take place. This chapter will examine mobile, system equipment, and operational costs. Also reviewed are marketing considerations that will affect the consumer demand for dual mode equipments.

7.1. MOBILE EQUIPMENT COSTS

It appears initial dual mode mobiles reaching the market in 1992 will be approximately 2 times the current cost (or approximately $600) of analog mobiles [1]. The increased cost is due to three factors: development cost, cost of production, and patent royalty cost.

7.1.1. Development Costs

Unlike well-established FM technology with limited digital signal processing, non-reoccurring engineering (NRE) development costs for digital cellular are high. Many companies have spent millions of dollars developing dual mode products. It is unlikely that the first generation of dual mode phones will recover their development costs. These NRE costs will be a high percentage of the price of the first dual mode mobile equipment. It is projected that the starting roll out of dual mode equipment will be 100,000 to 200,000 units due to the initial high cost of mobiles [2]. With the limited demand, it has been estimated that over $100/unit will be dedicated to recover NRE costs [3].

7.1.2. Cost of Production

Dual Mode units are much more complex than the older analog units and use expensive DSPs (digital signal processors). The cost up estimates have ranged from 15% [4] to over 400% [5] over the existing analog cost. A Dual Mode phone is composed of an analog transceiver and a new digital voice channel section. The primary hardware additions that significantly increase the cost are DSPs. A single DSP costs between $20-50, and several are required.

7.1.3. Patent Royalty Cost

Perhaps the most significant cost factor may be patent royalties. Cellular technology was originally developed and patented by AT&T [6]. To the author's knowledge, AT&T has never requested a single royalty payment for this fundamental technology. This is not the case for the IS-54 standard. Four companies have disclosed that they believe to have proprietary technology that is required to implement the standard [7]. One of these companies has already requested in excess of $10 per unit for licensing fees [8]. Patents have been discovered from other companies which also are required to implement the standard but have not been disclosed to the TIA [9].

7.2. SYSTEM EQUIPMENT COSTS

Network equipment changes will be required to provide the capability of digital transmission. These changes can be as simple as changing MSC software and base station RF equipments to installing an independent overlay system (see 6.6.4). Obviously, cost will vary with the implementation method selected. Some system equipment configurations, such as the use of repeaters, can significantly reduce equipment costs even in RSAs.

Many vendors are offering to support the retrofitting of existing cell site equipment to dual mode capability. This means an existing switch will receive new software and the base stations would receive new hardware. It has been estimated dual mode system equipment will be 1.5 times analog equipment [10].

To rapidly deploy a digital cellular system, it is possible to keep an existing analog system in operation and install a new overlayed digital system. This gives the cellular service provider the option of using another vendor who may be more competitive or who has a product available prior to the existing switch manufacturer. This option does not come without hidden costs. The overlay system approach uses the secondary dedicated control channels, reducing the total number of available control channels.

Since one RF channel can serve many users, either the number of base station RF equipment is decreased, or the system capacity may be increased. For example, a cell site which has 24 analog RF channels can convert 12 channels to full rate TDMA (3 users to 1 30 kHz RF channel) and now support 48 voice channels. With the introduction of the half rate TDMA channels (6 users to 1 30 kHz RF channel), the same cell site with 24 analog RF channels could convert 12 analog RF channels to half rate TDMA and now support 84 voice channels. A future consideration is the acceptance of DSI (digital speech interpolation) to allow the transmission of speech data only when a talker is actively speaking. This further doubles the capacity (assuming 50% voice activity) allowing the same 24 channel cell site to convert 12 channels to digital and have up to 156 voice channels.

Table 7.1 shows a sample of system equipment costs as TDMA technology evolves. In column 1, we see FM technology that supports one channel per carrier. Since approximately 20 subscribers can be supported per channel,[1] each RF channel cost is shared by 20 users. For the TDMA3 where each RF channel supports up to three users, each RF channel cost is shared by 60 subscribers. For the TDMA6 where each RF channel supports up to six users (half rate codec), each RF channel cost is shared by 120 subscribers. And perhaps the most optimal gain in the near future is the application of DSI (digital speech interpolation) which transmits only when speech information is available. This further reduces the cost per RF carrier by half, so the per channel cost is shared by 240 subscribers.

Table 7.1 Sample Cost Per Voice Channel

	FM	TDMA3	TDMA6	TDMA12
Tower and Bldg.	$500,000	$500,000	$500,000	$500,000
No. of RF Channels	50	50	50	50
No. of Voice Channels	50	150	300	600
Hardware cost/channel	$10,000	$15,000	$15,000	$15,000
Channels Costs	$500,000	$750,000	$750,000	$750,000
Total Costs	$1,000,000	$1,250,000	$1,250,000	$1,250,000
Loading	20:1	20:1	20:1	20:1
Total Customers	1,000	3,000	6,000	12,000
Cost per Customer	$1,000	$417	$208	$104

While it is not suggested that all of the available RF channels will be converted to digital in the near future, this sample table produces target costs that project a reasonable cost for cellular system equipment in the future.

The multiplexing of several radio channels through one RF equipment reduces the number of required RF equipments, power consumption, and system cooling requirements. This will also reduce cell site size and backup power supply (generator and battery) requirements, and ultimately, cost.

---

1 With the average airtime use per subscriber decreasing (see Shosteck, CSF, figures 2.1 & 2.2), it may be possible to support more than 40 subscribers per channel.

Another system equipment cost savings can result from the use of repeaters. Since each RF channel has an increased number of voice channels per RF channel, repeaters can be added liberally in place of additional cell sites. Figure 7.1 shows a large area which is covered with one expensive cell site and several inexpensive repeaters [11].

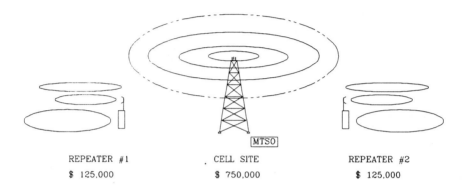

REPEATER #1	CELL SITE	REPEATER #2
$ 125,000	$ 750,000	$ 125,000

NOTE: THERE ARE NO LEASED COMMUNICATIONS LINKS
BETWEEN THE CELL SITE AND REPEATERS.

Figure 7.1 Dual Mode Cellular and Repeaters

7.3. OPERATIONAL COSTS

The use of efficient cellular technologies may reduce both fixed and operational costs. A reduction of operational costs is required to increase the success of the cellular systems for both the MSAs and RSAs. Each cell site or RF channel that is added increases fixed and operational costs. For analog cellular, as the number of subscribers increases where cell splitting occurs, the average cost per subscriber increases. For the proposed conversion to digital systems, as the number of subscribers increases, the average cost per subscribers decreases [12].

One of the main advantages of digital cellular is the reduction of operational costs by infrastructure savings. The operational cost benefits of installing digital equipment include a reduction in the total number of leased communication links, a lesser number of cell sites, reducing land leasing requirements, decreased base station power consumption, and less fraud due to advanced authentication procedures.

7.3.1. Communications Links

Digital signal processing for all the proposed technologies allows for a reduction in the number of required communications links. Voice information is compressed into a form much smaller than existing communication channels. This allows several users (up to 16 for half rate TDMA) to share one 64 kbps communications channel (DS0), significantly reducing the number of leased lines.

7.3.2. Land Leasing

In rural areas, exact locations for cell site towers are not required. The result is that land leasing is not a significant problem. In urban areas, and as systems mature, more exact locations for cell sites are required. This results in increased land leasing costs. By using a more efficient RF technology, one cell site can be used to serve more channels, limiting the total number of required cell sites.

7.3.3. Power Consumption

While each digital RF channel consumes more power than an analog RF channel, the overall system efficiency for TDMA digital cellular is greater due to the multiplexing of three voice channels on one RF amplifier. This results in a reduced total power consumption for base station RF amplifiers. This efficiency will double with the introduction of half rate codecs and double again with the use of DSI.

7.3.4. Cellular Fraud

It is estimated that cellular fraud in 1990 ranged between $100-400 million [13]. The new digital cellular standard has an advanced authentication capability which will limit the ability to gain fraudulent access to the cellular network.

7.4. DUAL MODE MARKETING CONSIDERATIONS

The cellular service providers encouraged the development of digital cellular technology to allow cost effective system capacity expansion. To obtain this cost savings, it is necessary to have a subscriber base that can use the advanced technology. The key marketing factors that will determine the success of dual mode cellular include the terminal cost to the consumer, consumer confidence, new features, retrofitting, availability of portables, and marketing of used equipment.

7.4.1. Terminal Cost to Consumer

In 1984-85, cellular mobile telephone prices hovered around $2000-$2500 [14]. In 1991, you could get a free cellular phone with the purchase of a hamburger at selected Big Boy Restaurants [15]. One of the primary reasons for the continued penetration of the cellular market is the declining terminal equipment costs and stable airtime charges [16]. The initial higher cost of dual mode mobiles will impact the roll out of Dual Mode units although the consumer may not see the higher cost. Mobile station equipment is often subsidized by the cellular service provider. The average subsidy in March 1990 was $197-$274 [17]. To help introduce digital cellular into cellular markets, subsidies may be increased for dual mode equipment. Many of the service providers are not concerned with the profit on mobile equipment as their goal is to gain service revenue. This results in the cellular service providers being the determining factor for the deployment of Dual Mode equipment in the field.

7.4.2. Consumer Confidence

To effectively deploy a new technology, the consumer must have confidence that the technology will endure. The next generation of cellular technology was required to operate on the old and new systems to maintain this consumer confidence [18].

7.4.3. New Features

Some of the significant features that sell phones today include: battery life, size, and service capabilities [19]. Dual mode cellular phones will have longer talk time, reasonable size, and lots of new features.

7.4.3.1. Battery Life

Because there are no changes in the control channel structure for dual mode phones, standby time should not be affected. Because there is a new digital traffic channel, talk time will vary between an analog voice channel and the digital traffic channel with the digital channel having longer talk time [20]. With the introduction of half rate speech coder technology (6 vs. 3 users per RF channel), talk time can be further doubled. Application of DSI in combination with half rate technology may allow talk times in excess of four hours with today's battery technology.

7.4.3.2. Size

While the first FM cellular telephone weighed over eighty pounds and required almost all of available trunk space, the first dual mode transceivers will be only slightly larger than their analog predecessors [21]. Their size will be reduced as production volumes allow for custom ASIC (application specific integrated circuit) development which will integrate the analog and digital processing sections. There is no reason that the dual mode transceivers cannot approach the same size as the analog cellular phones today [22].

7.4.3.3. Service Capabilities

The addition of new features increases the target market of cellular by offering more billable services. Some of the new features that have been added include calling number and connected number identification, distinctive alert, authentication and voice privacy, mobile assisted handoff (MAHO), and message waiting. Future features include advice of charging, discontinuous reception, advanced data transfer, and short message transmission.

Calling Number/Connected Number Identification allows presentation of the calling party's number or connected party's number either before a call is answered or during a conversation. Distinctive alert creates different sounds to indicate a different vertical service such as identification of key callers (e.g. boss or mother-in-law). Authentication involves significant processing of the mobile electronic serial number (ESN) and other subscriber mobile parameters so ESN capture and fraudulent use is virtually impossible. Encryption of speech data performs the scrambling of voice information so eavesdropping cannot occur by someone without a known code. A message waiting feature has been added to allow display of the number of messages received. Advice of charging will show the estimated cost of operation of the cellular phone prior to call origination. Discontinuous reception will push standby time well in excess of 100 hours. ISDN like interfacing will allow synchronous and asynchronous data transmission at data rates between 300-9600 baud. Short Message Transmission or Datagram will allow brief text messages, approximately up to one page of text, to be stored, printed, or displayed on a screen.

7.4.4. Retrofitting

One of the easiest ways to reduce blockage and quickly increase the system efficiency is by retrofitting high usage subscribers [23]. The cost of converting an analog subscriber to a dual mode subscriber includes the physical changing of the mobile and possibly an activation incentive. The challenge is to remove as many analog mobiles and replace them with dual mode units at a reasonable cost [24]. Retrofitting high usage subscribers will increase the total demand for dual mode mobile units for several years.

7.4.4.1. Equipment Installation

While new subscribers can expect the same installation requirements as the existing cellular phones, retrofit programs may require less installation effort if only a transceiver needs to be replaced [25]. This will allow for a 15 minute upgrade where the customer drives into a service center, the transceiver is changed, and questions are answered.[2]

7.4.4.2. Conversion Incentive

Dual mode cellular service provides superior voice quality and advanced features that are not offered by analog cellular equipments. It is possible that some consumers may pay more for this advanced technology, however, studies have shown consumer satisfaction with the analog system has been relatively stable [26]. This results in it being unlikely that a majority of consumers will pay several hundred dollars to replace their working cellular phone.

High commissions may be paid or a free replacement phone may be issued to a high usage subscriber as a conversion incentive. If a high incentive commission is given for the replacement of the analog phone, it may be possible to require the old analog phone to be returned to the cellular service provider to obtain the extra incentive.

7.4.5. Availability of Portables

The first cellular portable was introduced in 1984 by Motorola. It weighed 30 ozs. and had 30 minutes of talk time. In early August 1991, Motorola released the Micro-Tac Light weighing 7.7 ozs. [27] and offering 45 minutes of talk time. The additional DSP circuitry that is required for a TDMA dual mode portable weighs approximately 3 ozs. using commercially available DSPs [28]. The possibility exists for a 10 oz. TDMA dual mode portable within the near future.

---

2 This assumes a significant portion of the subscriber base having upgradeable analog units such as the Audiovox "A" series cellular phones.

The demand for portables is increasing. In some urban markets, this demand exceeds 50% [29]. This implies a continued growth of analog cellular in urban areas since microsize (approximately 10 ozs.) dual mode portables will not be immediately available.

7.4.6. Marketing of Used Equipment

With the retrofitting of system and mobile equipment, some of the older analog equipment can be marketed to recover conversion costs. The marketing of analog mobiles and portables is straightforward, but selling cellular systems is much more restricted.

7.4.6.1. Used Mobile Equipment

If a used analog phone is obtained via a retrofit program, a challenge exists as to what to do with the retrofitted customer's analog equipment. If it is allowed to re-enter the system, the analog subscriber base will increase defeating the purpose of the Dual Mode capacity gains. Today's market for used cellular equipment in the U.S. is approximately 5% [30]. With many new RSAs being installed in the U.S., it may be possible to allocate some mobile equipment to U.S. RSAs. Another possibility is to market the used equipment in offshore countries. Over 50 countries are U.S. AMPS compatible (see appendix IV). The logical choices are to either destroy the analog mobiles, market them overseas, or move them to other U.S. markets.

7.4.6.2. Used System Equipment

A market exists today for used system equipment [31]. A key element of the cellular system is the MTSO which is often referred to as the switch, which requires computer programs (software) to operate. This operating software is often leased and not sold. When a used switch is sold, the software cannot go with it. This results in a piece of equipment that is useless without software. While switch equipment may not be sold, the marketing of used towers and cell site equipment is a growing market [32].

7.5. SUMMARY

Dual mode cellular mobile, system equipment, and operational costs are different than their analog predecessor. Increased mobile equipment cost is due to three factors: development cost, cost of production (components), and patent royalty cost. System equipment costs will vary based on the implementation method selected. These deployments can be as simple as changing MSC software and base station RF equipment to installing an independent overlay system. The use of efficient digital cellular technologies may reduce operational costs. The operational cost benefits of installing digital equipment include a reduction in the total number of leased communication links, a lesser number of cell sites, reducing land leasing requirements, decreased base station power consumption, and less fraud due to advanced authentication procedures.

Digital cellular technology was developed to allow cost effective system capacity expansion. To obtain this cost savings, it is necessary to have a subscriber base that can use the advanced technology. The key marketing factors that will determine the success of dual mode cellular include the terminal cost to the consumer, consumer confidence, new features, retrofitting, availability of portables, and marketing of used equipment.

References:

[1] Telecommunications Industries Association Transition to Digital Symposium, "New Services and Capabilities," TIA, Orlando, FL, (Sept. 1991).

[2] Herschel Shosteck, personal communication, 25 September 1991.

[3] Telecommunications Industries Association Transition to Digital Symposium, "New Services and Capabilities," TIA, Orlando, FL, (Sept. 1991).

[4] Slekys, Dr. Arunas G., "What's Ahead Worldwide for Digital Cellular," *Mobile Radio Technology*, (May 1990).

[5] Shosteck, personal communication, 25 September 1991.

[6] Patent 3,663,762, "Mobile Communication System," May 1972.

[7] Letter to TIA voting members from Eric J. Schimmel, 21 November 1990.

[8] TIA, "New Services and Capabilities," (Sept. 1991).

[9] Patent 5,008,953, "Mobile Station Link Supervision Utilizing Digital Voice Color Codes," April 1991.

[10] TIA, "Transition and Compatibility," (Sept. 1991).

[11] DeVaney, David. Vice President of Engineering, Astronet Corporation. Interview, 27 June 1991.

[12] Stover, Dawn. "Cellular Goes Digital," *Popular Science*, (January 1990), p. 53.

[13] TIA, "Authentication and Voice Privacy," (Sept. 1991).

[14] Dr. George Calhoun, *Digital Cellular Radio*, (MA: Artech House, 1988), p. 69.

[15] Stuart F. Crump, *Cellular Sales and Marketing*, (Washington, D.C.: Creative Communications Inc., August 1991), Vol. 5, No. 8, p. 2.

[16] Hilbert Chan and C. Vinodrai, "The Transition to Digital Cellular," (IEEE 1990 Vehicular Technology Conference), p. 191.

[17] Herschel Shosteck Associates LTD, "The Retail Market of Cellular Telephones," Vol. 7, No. 2, Chapter 15, (December 1991), Figure 15.4.

[18] CTIA Winter Exposition, John Stupka, "Technology Update," (Reno, Nevada, 1990).

[19] TIA, "New Services and Capabilities," (Sept. 1991).

[20] *Ibid.*

[21] Spivak, Michael, "Digital Cellular Creates Added Challenges," *Installation News*, (June 1991), pp. 60-65.

[22] TIA, "New Services and Capabilities," (Sept. 1991).

[23] *Ibid.*

[24] Day Group, Newsletter, September 1990, pp. 4-7.

[25] Spivak, "Digital Cellular Creates Added Challenges," pp. 60-65.

[26] "Cellular Subscribers and Forecasts," Vol. 5, No. 1, Figures 2.3 & 2.4.

[27] Crump, *Cellular Sales and Marketing*, p. 1.

[28] TIA, "New Services and Capabilities," (Sept. 1991).

[29] Danaeé, David, Director, Product Planning, McCaw Corporation. Interview, April 1990.

[30] Shosteck, "The Retail Market of Cellular Telephones," Chapter 10, Figures 10.3 & 10.4.

[31] Chris Cherney, PLI, personal communication, March 1990.

[32] *Ibid.*

Chapter 8

World Cellular Technologies

8.1. WORLD SYSTEMS INTRODUCTION

Over 70 countries have at least one cellular system in operation (see Appendix IV). While the concept of cellular, frequency reuse is used in all of these systems, the physical parameters and feature capabilities differ. This chapter will define parameters and describe some of the more significant differences.

An allocation of radio spectrum may be divided into a group of channels. Generally, there are three types of channel division multiple access: Frequency Division Multiple Access (FDMA), Time Division Multiple Access (TDMA), and Spread Spectrum code division multiple access (CDMA). FDMA systems divide radio spectrum into channel bandwidths where each frequency bandwidth supports one voice channel. TDMA systems further divide an RF channel bandwidth into time slots which are shared between a number of users. Spread spectrum channels encode a unique signal with the speech data and transmit on a very large bandwidth so users can simultaneously transmit on the same frequency bandwidth with only minimal interference.

8.2. FREQUENCY DIVISION MULTIPLE ACCESS (FDMA)

For FDMA systems, each RF channel carries one single conversation. While several modulation strategies have been available, FM (frequency modulation) is the method used for all major cellular systems due to its high resistance to noise. FM transceivers have a lower mobile subscriber unit complexity than other proposed technologies [1]. This is traded off with higher shared system costs because only a limited number of subscribers can share the network equipment cost of each RF channel [2]. An additional requirement of FDMA systems is that the transmitter and receiver must operate simultaneously. Frequency duplexing circuitry is necessary. In turn, this increases size, cost, and power consumption.

In some FDMA systems, channel interleaving has been used to allow an increase in the reuse of frequencies. Interleaving allows transmitters to be assigned to frequencies other than the center of the channel frequency band. This is beneficial because for FM modulation, the average occupied bandwidth is much less than the allocated frequency bandwidth. RF channels can then be used more often increasing system capacity. World systems using

FDMA channelization include AMPS, NAMPS, TACS, NMT-450, NMT-900, C-NET, and RC-2000.

8.2.1. AMPS

The AMPS (advanced mobile phone service) system was invented by AT&T [3]. The AMPS acronym is currently accepted for the evolved analog cellular system network EIA-553 as described in chapters 1 through 3.

The original bandwidth for the AMPS system was 40 MHz, allowing only 666 duplex channels. Shortly after the commercial introduction of AMPS, it became apparent that cost effective expansion was becoming a challenge. In 1986, this resulted in the allocation of 10 MHz of additional spectrum to be shared among the existing cellular service providers [4]. Today, the AMPS system is in use in over 50 different countries.

Significant EIA-553 parameters include:

Maximum Mobile Output Power: 4/1.6/.6 Watts

Bandwidth per channel: 30 kHz

Number of channels: 832/RF – 790/Voice

Total Bandwidth: 25 MHz x 2

Data transmission rate: 10 kbps

Frequency range: 824-849 MHz/869-894 MHz

8.2.2. NAMPS - Narrowband FDMA

Since the 1940s, radio spectrum efficiency has been increased by reducing the allocated channel frequency bands [5]. It has been demonstrated that FDMA analog units can be modified to provide a narrow channel bandwidth allowing approximately a 3 times capacity gain [6]. The disadvantages of narrowband technology include increased network RF equipment cost, increased frequency planning, and reduced voice quality.

Significant NAMPS parameters include:

Maximum Mobile Output Power: 4/1.6/.6 Watts

Bandwidth per channel: 10 kHz

Number of channels: 832/RF – 2370/Voice

Total Bandwidth: 25 MHz x 2

Data transmission rate: 10k/200/100

Frequency range: 824-849 MHz/869-894 MHz

8.2.3. TACS - Totally Accessible Communications System

TACS is similar to AMPS with channel spacing changed to 25 kHz and data signaling rate changed to 8 kHz. The TACS system also had cost effective expansion problems. Additional spectrum was awarded, and with the addition of new features, this resulted in ETACS. Unfortunately, the available spectrum was not adjacent to the existing frequency band which now requires a more complex duplexer filter. Several variations of the TACS system exist. These vary from different frequency allocation, reduced maximum FM deviation, and channel interleaving.

Significant TACS parameters include:

System Type	Base TX frequency channel 1	Mobile TX number of channel 1	Maximum spacing channels	Channel offset	Duplex
E-TACS	935.0125	890.0125	2047	25 kHz	45
CTACS I	460.5000	450.5000	120	25 kHz	10
CTACS II	924.0125	879.0125	800	25 kHz	45
J-TACS	860.0125	915.0125	798	12.5 kHz	−55
N-TACS	860.0125	915.0125	2160	12.5 kHz	−55
TACS	935.0125	890.0125	600	25 kHz	45

Maximum Mobile Output Power: 7/2.8/1.1 (TACS, ETACS, CTACS)

2.8/1.1/.45 (JTACS, NTACS)

Data transmission rate: 8 kbps

8.2.4. Nordic Mobile Telephone NMT-450

NMT-450 was introduced in the Scandanavian countries in 1981 (7). Its unique features include control channel signaling at a very low rate and messages not being repeated. Although there is a control channel, all channels in the NMT-450 system can be used as voice channels.

Significant NMT-450 parameters include:

System Country	Mobile TX frequency channel 1	Maximum number of channels	Channel 1 low/high	Channel spacing	Duplex Offset MHz
Denmark	453.000	180	Low	+ 25 kHz	+ 10
Sweden	453.000	180	Low	+ 25 kHz	+ 10
Norway	453.000	180	Low	+ 25 kHz	+ 10
Finland	453.000	180	Low	+ 25 kHz	+ 10
Iceland	453.000	180	Low	+ 25 kHz	+ 10
Holland	451.310	222	Low	+ 20 kHz	+ 10
Belgium	451.310	222	Low	+ 20 kHz	+ 10
Luxemburg	451.310	222	Low	+ 20 kHz	+ 10
Austria	455.730	222	High	–20 kHz	+ 10
Spain	454.325	180	Low	+ 25 kHz	+ 10
Malaysia	452.000	180	Low	+ 25 kHz	+ 10
Saudi Arabia Band I	458.775	180	Low	+ 25 kHz	–10
Saudi Arabia Band II	438.400	180	Low	+ 25 kHz	–10
Indonesia	479.000	225	Low	+ 20 kHz	+ 10
Tailand	479.000	225	Low	+ 20 kHz	+ 10
Oman	438.400	180	Low	+ 25 kHz	–10
Tunisia	453.000	180	Low	+ 25 kHz	+ 10
Turkey	415.500	180	Low	+ 25 kHz	+ 10

Maximum Mobile Output Power: 15/2 Watts (except Austria & Spain)
12.5/2 Watts (Austria & Spain)

Bandwidth per channel: 25 kHz

Number of channels: 180/RF – 180/Voice (220 Netherlands)

Data transmission rate: 1200

Frequency range: 420-480

8.2.5. Nordic Mobile Telephone NMT-900

The NMT-900 system has penetrated into several European countries. It features 12.5 kHz channel interleaving.

Significant NMT-900 parameters include:

Maximum Mobile Output Power: 6/1 Watt (except France & Turkey)

7/1 Watt (France)

Bandwidth per channel: 25 kHz

Data transmission rate: 1200 bps

Number of channels: 2023

Frequency range: 890 to 915/935-960 MHz

8.2.6. CNET

The CNET system is used in Germany. Unique features include 10 kHz and 12.5 kHz synthesizer steps. Duplex channel separation is 10 MHz.

Significant CNET parameters include:

Maximum Mobile Output Power: 15 W/750 mW

Bandwidth per channel: 20 kHz

Data transmission rate: 5.2 kbps

Frequency range: 451 to 455.74/461-465.74 MHz

8.2.7. RC2000

The RC2000 system is a hybrid cellular/trunking system used in France. It supports both simplex and duplex mobiles on a number of locally allocated bands in the UHF and VHF regions.

Significant RC2000 parameters include:

Fixed Transmission Frequencies

Band 1:	424.8000 to 427.9875 MHz
Band 2:	Reserved
Band 3:	169.8000 to 173.4875 MHz
Band 4:	176.5000 to 178.6875 MHz
Band 5:	178.7000 to 181.0875 MHz
Band 6:	181.1000 to 183.4875 MHz
Band 7:	200.5000 to 202.6875 MHz
Band 8:	202.7000 to 205.0875 MHz
Band 9:	205.1000 to 207.4875 MHz
Band 10:	208.5000 to 210.6875 MHz
Band 11:	210.7000 to 213.0875 MHz
Band 12:	213.1000 to 215.4875 MHz

Mobile Transmission Frequencies

Band 1:	414.8000 to 417.9875 MHz
Band 2:	Reserved
Band 3:	165.2000 to 168.9975 MHz
Band 4:	184.5000 to 186.6875 MHz
Band 5:	186.7000 to 189.0875 MHz
Band 6:	189.1000 to 191.4875 MHz
Band 7:	192.5000 to 194.6875 MHz
Band 8:	194.7000 to 197.0875 MHz
Band 9:	197.1000 to 199.4875 MHz
Band 10:	216.5000 to 218.6875 MHz
Band 11:	218.7000 to 221.0875 MHz
Band 12:	221.1000 to 223.4875 MHz

Number of Channels

Bands 1 & 3:	256
Bands 4, 7, & 10:	176
Bands 5, 6, 8, 9, 11 & 12:	192

Maximum Mobile Output Power: 11 W or 2 W

Bandwidth per channel: 12.5 kHz

Data transmission rate: 1200 bps

8.3. TIME DIVISION MULTIPLE ACCESS (TDMA)

Time division multiplexing divides an RF carrier into time slots to be shared by several users. Speech intervals are converted to digital form and compressed in time to fit in a mobile transmit burst. These mobile time bursts are aligned with an assigned time slot. Some of the advantages of TDMA transmission include burst transmission (power saving), time division duplexing, slow frequency hopping, improved speech quality, and enhanced data services.

Burst Transmission only requires the transmitter to be on for a short period which increases battery life. Time Division Duplexing (TDD) is the ability to transmit and receive at different times so simultaneous transmission and reception is not required. The mobile's terminal size and cost are reduced because the duplexer can be replaced with an RF switch. This enables one antenna to switch between the transmit and receive sections as needed. Slow frequency hopping is possible by transmitting the bursts at different frequencies to overcome the problem of slow moving mobiles experiencing a deep fade condition. By the use of digital transmission with error detection and error correction capabilities, improved speech quality is obtained in poor service areas [8]. Finally, with reliable data transmission, enhanced vertical services may be added liberally.

Some disadvantages of TDMA digital cellular include higher mobile complexity, and no RF channel interleaving. TDMA mobile units are more complex than analog mobiles due to the extensive digital signal processing. To transmit digital information efficiently, the entire bandwidth is usually occupied so no channel interleaving is possible.

Future enhancements of TDMA systems include lower bit rate codecs and digital speech interpolation (DSI). Lower bit rate codecs will allow more users to share an RF channel. Digital speech interpolation allows bursts to be transmitted only when speech information is available, allowing more users to share an RF channel. World systems using TDMA channelization include IS-54 (U.S. Digital), GSM, and PCN.

8.3.1. IS-54 (U.S. Digital)

The first U.S. digital cellular phones will be dual mode to allow access to the new digital channels but also maintain backward compatibility with the existing EIA-553 standard. In the future when digital service is readily available, digital only mobiles will appear. While the U.S. dual mode cellular permits efficient operation of the voice/traffic channel, the dual mode control channel still requires simultaneous transmission and reception. The digital traffic channels will support TDD transmission for the digital only system.

Significant IS-54 parameters include:

Maximum Mobile Output Power: 4/1.6/.6 Watts

Bandwidth per channel: 30 kHz

Number of channels: 832 RF – 2370/voice

Total Bandwidth: 25 MHz x 2

Data transmission rate: 10 kbps

Gross channel transmission rate: 48.6 kbps

Frequency range: 824-849 MHz/869-894 MHz

8.3.2. Groupe Speciale Mobile (GSM)

In 1982 the Conference of European Postal and Telecommunications (CEPT) administrations formed "Groupe Speciale Mobile" (GSM), presently a working group in the European Telecommunications Standards Institute (ETSI), to create a standard for a common European Digital Cellular System [9]. Several European countries use this standard to allow international roaming. Its features are very similar to the IS-54 standard. However, unlike the U.S. dual mode digital phones, the first European digital cellular phones will be single mode, allowing access only to the new digital channels.

Unique features of the GSM system include a high data rate transfer, short bursts, slow frequency hopping, open network architecture (ONA), and smart card technology.

A high data rate of 270 kbps allows for a minimized speech processing delay and short time bursts to overcome the limitation of a changing RF channel thus reducing equalizer requirements. Slow frequency hopping adds frequency diversity, minimizing long RF fades. With its open network architecture a variety of vendors can supply different sections of the GSM system equipment. GSM requires the subscriber to use a smart card. All the necessary information to update the system and operate the phone is contained on the card.

The RF frequencies, digital signal processing, and signalling methods are much different than the U.S. Digital Cellular System. The GSM specification is much more detailed and does not allow the design flexibility of the U.S. IS-54 standard. The only similarity is that both systems are TDMA.

Significant GSM parameters include:

Maximum Mobile Output Power: 10/8/5/2 Watts

Bandwidth per channel: 200 kHz

Number of channels: 992

Total Bandwidth: 25 MHz x 2

Data transmission rate: 13 kbps

Gross channel transmission rate: 270.883 kbps

Frequency range: 890-915 MHz/935-960 MHz

8.3.3. PCN (England)

A new competing cellular system is being introduced in England. PCN will use the GSM TDMA standard in the 1.7-1.8 GHz range.

Significant PCN parameters include:

Maximum Mobile Output Power: 1W/250 mw

Bandwidth per channel: 200 kHz

Number of channels: 2976

Total Bandwidth: 75 MHz x 2

Data transmission rate: 13 kbps

Gross channel transmission rate: 270.883 kbps

Frequency range: 1710-1785 MHz/1805-1880 MHz

8.4. CODE DIVISION MULTIPLE ACCESS (CDMA)

CDMA was developed by a pair of ITT engineers shortly after World War II. CDMA has been predominantly military due to its inherent data transmission security [10]. Only recently did CDMA enter the commercial marketplace with satellite products like Omnitracs™.[1] However, CDMA is a more abstract technology and is not generally applied by many manufacturers. Unique features of CDMA include simplification of frequency planning, unequal cell loading, soft handoff, soft capacity limit, system capacity improvement, flexible data rates, and increased resistance to Rayleigh fading.

8.4.1. CDMA Advantages

Controversy exists on the true advantage of using CDMA in a mobile environment. The advantages claimed by the CDMA proponents are very interesting, especially from a service provider's point of view. For analog cellular, frequency planning is a costly process and gets more complicated with cell site divisions. Unlike the cellular frequency reuse technology for FDMA and TDMA, CDMA allows each cell to have a reuse factor of 1. This means each cell can reuse the same dedicated bandwidth without any frequency planning.[2]

The demand for service in a cellular system may be unequal by time of day and traffic conditions. CDMA allows allocation of more channels in one cell with varying traffic densities. This dynamic channel allocation is more complex for FDMA/TDMA systems as it involves frequency planning.

CDMA also allows the mobile to communicate between two base stations simultaneously. When the voice quality from the targeted cell site is sufficient, the handoff takes place and no voice interruption occurs.

With the U.S. IS-54 TDMA system, when the number of time slots have all been assigned, it is a finite limit. With CDMA, as the number of users increases beyond the optimal limit, the voice quality gradually diminishes for all users. This allows overloading of the system. Packetized speech utilizing

---

1   Omnitracs is a trademark of Qualcomm Corporation.
2   Some frequency planning may be necessary due to adjacent systems.

Digital Speech Interpolation (DSI) offers similar overloading possibilities to TDMA systems.

Increased system serving capacity claims vary from 2.0 [11], up to a 40 times increase when compared to the FDMA cellular system [12].

Another advantage is that CDMA allows many users to have different data rates without introducing processing delays. TDMA can provide several data rates, but it is not easily adaptable for high data rates.

Rayleigh fades are a result of multipath propagation. Fades are dependent on frequency so when a broad band spectrum is used, a Rayleigh fade results in only some bits which cannot be decoded. With a good spread spectrum system, there will be minimal fades to the user. Portable cellular FDMA users in fringe areas constantly move around to avoid fades. Standing within a deep fade for too long using an FDMA narrowband transceiver may result in a dropped call.

8.4.2. CDMA Challenges

While CDMA has many significant advantages, it still has some challenges to overcome. A fully loaded terrestrial system has not been demonstrated with independent adjacent systems in operation. Substantial challenges include power level control, dynamic power range, and unequal cell diameters.

CDMA requires the signal strength of each mobile to be approximately the same at the Base Station. The received level of each mobile must be within approximately 1 dB of each other [13].

The mobile units must also have large dynamic range. An 80 dB dynamic range has been suggested for the CDMA power level control [14].

Interference is a limiting factor in mobile units operating in adjacent cells where one cell is significantly larger than another. The power level interference problem could be overcome by either using a coordinated frequency hopping spread spectrum approach where the power density spectrum is coordinated resulting in less interference to adjacent cells [15].

8.4.3. Working Commercial CDMA Systems

Qualcomm has had a working CDMA satellite system for several years. Omnitracs transmits and receives data and provides tracking information to its customers. Figure 8.1 shows the Qualcomm Omnitracs System.

Figure 8.1 Omnitracs System (courtesy of Qualcomm Corp.)

Omnipoint Data was the first to develop a direct sequence CDMA cordless phone. The first Omnipoint system offered flexible data rates from 8 kbps to 192 kbps in 8 kbps increments. Higher data rates are available now. Figure 8.2 shows the 4 channel Omnipoint data CDMA base station and handheld unit.

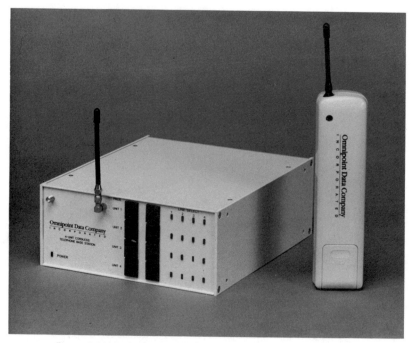

Figure 8.2 Handheld CDMA Telephone (courtesy Omnipoint Data)

8.5. SUMMARY

Over 70 countries have at least one cellular system in operation. The physical parameters and feature capabilities differ significantly among some of these systems. There are generally three types of channel division multiple access available today: Frequency Division Multiple Access (FDMA), Time Division Multiple Access (TDMA), and Spread Spectrum code division multiple access (CDMA).

For FDMA systems, each RF channel carries one single conversation and almost all existing cellular systems use FM (frequency modulation). FM transceivers are less complex than TDMA and CDMA technologies. The tradeoff of FM lower complexity is higher system fixed and operational costs. World systems using FDMA channelization include AMPS, NAMPS, TACS/ETACS, NMT-450, NMT-900, C-NET, and RC-2000.

Time division multiplexing divides an RF carrier into time slots which are shared by several users. Speech information is converted to digital form and compressed in time to fit in a transmit burst. Some of the advantages of

TDMA transmission include power saving burst transmission, multiplexing several users on the same RF channel, slow frequency hopping, improved speech quality, and enhanced data services. Some disadvantages of TDMA digital cellular include higher mobile complexity, and no RF channel interleaving. World systems using TDMA channelization include IS-54 (U.S. Digital), GSM, and PCN.

CDMA is a more abstract technology and is not generally applied by many manufacturers. Controversy exists on the true advantages of using CDMA in a mobile environment. Unique features of CDMA include simplification of frequency planning, unequal cell loading, soft handoff, soft capacity limit, system capacity improvement, flexible data rates, and increased resistance to Rayleigh fading. Substantial challenges include power level control, dynamic power range, and unequal cell diameters. CDMA products available today include Omnitracs™ and Omnipoint Data 4 channel cordless phone system.

References:

[1] CTIA Narrow AMPS Forum, Chicago, IL, 9 December 1990.

[2] Dr. George Calhoun, *Digital Cellular Radio*, (MA: Artech House, 1988), p. 368.

[3] *Ibid.*, pp. 426-427.

[4] William Lee, *Mobile Cellular Telecommunications Systems*, (McGraw Hill, 1989), p. 6.

[5] Calhoun, pp. 298-299.

[6] CTIA Narrow AMPS Forum, Chicago, IL, 9 December 1990.

[7] Walter Miller, Ericsson Corp., personal communications, 24 October 1991.

[8] Telecommunications Industries Association Transition to Digital Symposium, John Stupka, (Orlando, FL, September 1991).

[9] TR45.3.2.5/91.09.19.07, TIA, *"Summary of Synchronous Data Transmission in the GSM Cellular Network,"(Albany, New York, September, 1991).*

[10] Dr. George Calhoun, *Digital Cellular Radio*, (MA: Artech House, 1988), pp. 341-344.

[11] IEEE Seminar, UCSD, *"TDMA Cellular,"* Mike Parr, (12 December 1990).

[12] National Engineering Consortium ComForum, *"Worldwide Personal Communications,"* (Dallas, Texas, June 27-28).

[13] IEEE Seminar, Mike Parr.

[14] Strich, Eli, Qualcomm. Interview, November 1990.

[15] Dixon, Robert, *Spread Spectrum Systems*, (Wiley, 1984), p. 77.

Appendix I - Definitions

Abbreviated Alert - An alert order that informs the user that a previous function selected is still active.

Access - A process where the mobile station competes to gain the attention of the system to obtain service.

Access Channel - Redefined to be Analog Access Channel.

Access Overload Class (ACCOLC) - A class assigned to a mobile to limit its access attempts in an overloaded system. The overhead message contains an overload field which corresponds to the access overload class assigned to the mobile. When the system becomes overloaded, the overhead message will begin to remove groups of mobiles accessing the system.

Adjacent Channel - A channel +/-30kHz from the current channel.

Adjacent Channel Interference - This occurs when the spectral power distribution from an adjacent channel creates noise or errors in the channel being used by the mobile or base station.

Advanced Mobile Phone Service (AMPS) - The service that is available in the United States and over 33 other countries today.

Advanced Radio Technology Subcommittee (ARTS) - Sponsored by the CTIA to study the industry needs, technology available, and manufacturers' support to develop new cellular technology.

Alert - An order sent to the mobile that informs the user that a call is to be received.

Alert with info - An alert message sent on the digital channel.

Alert with info Ack - A message sent back on the digital traffic channel that acknowledges the Alert with info order.

Alternate Channel - A cellular channel +/-60 kHz from the current channel.

Analog Access Channel - A cellular system channel that uses FSK (Frequency Shift Keying) to pass data control signals between the Mobile and Base. This control channel is used by the mobile to inform the system that it wants to obtain service.

Analog Cellular - An industry term given to today's existing cellular system. It involves transmission of voice information in a similar method to that of an FM radio.

Analog Color Code - One of three audio tones mixed in with the voice channel to distinguish the channel from interfering co-channels.

Analog Control Channel - A channel designated by the cell site to control operations of an analog and dual mode cellular phone. A control channel can be divided into paging and access functions.

Analog Mobile - A mobile unit which is only capable of Analog Cellular service.

Analog Voice Channel - A cellular system channel that operates by using FM (Frequency Modulation) to pass voice and data control signals between the Mobile and Base.

Audit - An order generated by the system which determines if the mobile is active within the system.

AUTH1 - An algorithm used to encrypt the ESN for transmission. Its inputs are the ESN (Electronic Serial Number), PIN (Personal Identification Number), and RAND (Random Number Sent by the System).

Authentication - A process during which information is exchanged between a Mobile Station and a Base Station to allow a cellular service provider to confirm the true identity thus inhibiting fraudulent use of the radio system.

Backhauling - The completion of a voice connection between a cell site and MTSO often requires the use of the landline network system. A fee must be paid for the use of these lines. Backhauling is the carrying of cellular calls between the cell sites and the MTSO via a landline network prior to reaching the PSTN.

Base Station - A controlling transmitting station that provides service to cellular mobile units. It is sometimes called a Land Station or Cell Site.

Bearer Services - Telecommunications services that provide facilities for the transport of user information without functional processing of the user data.

Bit Error Rate (BER) - The ratio of bits received in error with respect to the total number of bits transmitted.

Blocking Probability - The percentage of calls that cannot be completed within a one hour period due to capacity limitations. For example, if within one hour 100 users attempt accessing the system, and two attempts fail, the blocking probability is 2 percent.

Burst Collisions - The problem of transmit bursts originating from mobiles overlapping in time when received at the Base Station. This is due to the propagation time. Dynamic time alignment was created to solve this challenge.

Busy-Idle Bits - Bits that are time multiplexed with the forward control channels to indicate the access channel of the system is busy.

Busy Idle Status Field - A field sent in the overhead message train which informs the mobile of which access method to use when obtaining service from the system. If the bit is set high, the mobile must monitor the Busy-Idle bits to determine if the system is busy. When the bit is set low, the mobile attempts access without monitoring the Busy-Idle bits.

Carrier - A service provider of cellular service; RF energy emitted from a transmitter assembly.

Carrier-to-Noise Ratio - The ratio of the carrier with respect to the thermal noise.

Carrier-to-Interference Ratio (C/I) - The ratio of the carrier with respect to the combined interference due to adjacent and co-channel interference.

Carrier - A company that provides phone service to mobile subscribers. Only two carriers exist in a given area. Also known as service provider. Also means the RF transmitter frequency.

Cell Site - A radio tower and associated equipment that converts phone lines to radio signals for transmission to mobile phones.

Cell Splitting - A method to increase system capacity by the division of assigned radio areas. Each cell site (radio tower) can provide a limited number of channels. To increase the total number of channels available in a given area, it is possible to divide an area by adding additional radio towers.

Cellular Geographic Service Area (CGSA) - The area licensed by the FCC to a service provider. It is based on Metropolitan Statistical Areas or New England Metropolitan Areas.

Cellular Mobile Carriers (CMC) - The service providers that are licensed by the FCC to provide service in the CSGA. There are two CMCs authorized for each CGSA.

Cellular Subscriber Station (CSS) - Another name for Mobile Station. This is the preferred term to network providers due to Mobile Stations may be fixed in location.

Channel - May have two meanings: logical and physical. The physical channel is composed of 2 frequency bands separated by 45 MHz and with a bandwidth of 30 kHz. The logical channel is a throughput of information on that physical channel. A physical channel can be divided into many logical channels.

Co-channel - A channel being re-used at another cell site. This is allowed due to the attenuation of the signal because of the distance.

Co-channel Interference - A channel that is used by another cell site on the same frequency which interferes with the current channel. This is caused by insufficient attenuation of distance.

Channel Quality Message (CQM(1,2)) - Messages sent on the digital channel to provide the base station with channel quality information. This information can contain the RSSI (Received Signal Strength Indication) or BER (Bit Error Rate).

Coder/Decoder (Codec) - A process of compressing and expanding information so the transmission can be more efficient. By the use of this, digital voice information is characterized and reduced.

Coded Digital Voice Color Code (CDVCC) [Field, 12 bits] - The DVCC that has been coded by 12,8 hamming code. It can represent 255 different codes and identifies a channel from its interferers.

Coherence Bandwidth - A bandwidth in which either the phases or amplitudes of two received signals have a high degree of similarity.

Combined Paging and Access - This allows the combining of paging and access functions. This allows one channel to broadcast both paging messages while the reverse another channel allows system access within the same cell site. This leaves the paging channel free to only send system overhead and paging messages.

Combined Paging and Access (CPA) [Field] - This is a field in the forward overhead message which informs the mobile if the system has combined paging and access channels. If this bit is set to 1, the mobile must obtain access on the same control channel it receives the paging message on. If this bit is set to 0, the mobile must tune to an authorized access channel to obtain service.

Combiner - Used in Base Stations to couple different frequencies to one antenna.

Confirm Initial Traffic Channel {Task} - When the mobile station is assigned to a voice/traffic channel, it must confirm the message that it is being assigned within the cellular channel. If the assigned channel is not in the cellular band, it must re-initialize.

Continuous Transmission - A mode of operation where the mobile does not cycle its power level down when the modulating signal amplitude is low.

Control Channel - A cellular system channel dedicated to sending and/or receiving controlling messages between the Base and Mobile stations. (See Section Call Processing and RF Channel)

Control Mobile Attenuation Code (CMAC) [Field] - Used in a message sent to the mobile from the base which assigns the mobile to an absolute (specified) power level. This is important in small diameter cells where the mobile must access the system at a low power level to prevent co-channel interference with other control channels.

Convolutional Coding - A forward error correction method used to provide for correction of data that has been corrupted in transmission. This is accomplished by sending redundant information which allows for reconstruction of the original signal.

Coupler - See Combiner.

Cross Talk - A problem where the audio from one communications channel is imposed on another channel.

Cyclic Redundancy Check (CRC) - An error detection and/or correction method used to determine if a block or string of bits was received correctly.

Cyclic Redundancy Check (CRC) Generator - A function used to create a CRC data word. This word being a function of the data to be sent is used to verify the accuracy and may be used to correct some of the bits when in error.

Dead Spot - An area within a service area where the signal strength is significantly reduced. This is primarily due to terrain and obstructions. Dead spots are generally eliminated by the use of repeaters or relocation of the cell site.

Dedicated Control Channels - A nationwide allocated set of cellular channels that must be used only for control messages between the Base and Mobile station. For the wireline service these channels are 333 to 354. For the non-wireline service, the control channels are 332 to 311. (See Section Call Processing)

Delay Spread - A product of multipath propagation where symbols become distorted and eventually will overlap due to the same signal being received at a different time. It becomes a significant problem in mountainous areas where signals are reflected at great distances.

Digital Cellular - An industry term given to the new cellular technology that transmits voice information in digital form. This differs from Analog cellular in the method the transmission of voice/data information is represented by digital signals.

Digital Color Code (DCC) [Field] - This is a field which corresponds to the SAT code assigned to the cell site which is controlling the mobile. The mobile matches this code to the received SAT frequency to ensure it has locked on to the correct channel.

Digital Only Unit - A mobile phone that will only be capable of using the new digital signals. This will not be available for several years.

Digital Speech Interpolation (DSI) - A voice detecting system which allows transmission only when speech or data information is to be sent.

Digital Voice Color Code (DVCC) [Field] - Provides a unique code from the base station which identifies its channel from co-channels.

Digital Voice Color Code Status - This is a logical variable contained within the mobile. It can be enabled or disabled dependent on if a match occurs with incoming DVCC. Every burst contains a DVCC field. The mobile must transmit the DVCCs (stored value) even if it does not agree with incoming DVCC.

Discontinuous Transmission (DTX) - A method where the mobile changes its power level as a result of the input level of its modulating signal. This allows conservation of power when the modulating level is low or no data is to be transmitted.

Discontinuous Transmission (DTX) [Field] - A field included in the overhead message and reverse control channel message which indicates the base and the mobile are capable of discontinuous transmission respectively.

Diversity Reception - The process of combining or selecting one of two stronger of the signals received by two antennas. These antennas are usually separated by a distance that is a function of the wavelength.

Doppler - A frequency offset that is a result of a moving antenna relative to a transmitted signal.

Dotting - Used to synchronize the mobile. This acts like a: "wake up, a message is coming!" It then provides a standard sequence which allows the mobile time to synchronize to the incoming message.

Dual Mode Cellular - The combination of an Analog cellular unit and Digital cellular section into one cellular phone. It allows operation of the phone in the existing system as well as the new system when it becomes available.

Electromagnetic Interference (EMI) - Magnetic fields that interfere with the operation of the cellular phones. This includes any frequencies generated that interfere.

Equalization - A process which modifies the receiver parameters to compensate for changing radio frequency conditions. Primarily used to compensate for multipath propagation (see section RF channel).

Erlang - Amount of voice connection time with reference to one hour. For example, a 6 minute call is .1 Erlang.

Extended Protocol - Optional extended capability of the signaling messages which provide for the addition of new system features.

Extended Time Division Multiple Access - A time division cellular system which utilizes DSI (Digital Speech Interpolation) which allows transmission only when speech or data information is to be sent. When transmission is inhibited, the same channel and time slot can be shared by other users.

Fast Associated Control Channel (FACCH) - A logical signaling channel which is created by replacing speech data with signaling data in short periods of time.

Field - A dedicated number of bits within a message or data stream which is dedicated to specific functions.

Flash Request - A request to invoke a special processing function. Analog cellular only allowed flash requests from the mobile to the base. Dual Mode cellular allows flash requests in both directions.

Flash With Info - A flash message sent over the digital traffic channel. This function allows an indication that the originator needs special processing.

Forward Analog Control Channel (FOCC) - The Analog control channel which is from the base station to the mobile station.

Forward Analog Voice Channel (FVC) - The Analog voice/traffic channel which is from the base station to the mobile station.

Frame - Six slots are linked together to compose one frame. Any one or any combination of frames can be assigned to a single user.

Frequency Planning - The selection and assignment of channel frequencies to cell site equipments which minimize the interference levels they create with adjacent and alternate cell site equipments.

Frequency Reuse - The ability to reuse channels on the same frequency. This is possible due to the attenuation of the signals by distance.

Full Duplex - Transferring of voice/data in both directions at the same time. This becomes confusing in a TDMA system because information is reconstructed to allow transfer of voice information in both directions at the same time although actual transmission does not occur simultaneously.

Full Rate - The process where 2 slots per 6 slot frame is used to convey all speech or data within a 40 msec interval.

Group Identification - A subset of the system identification (SID) which identifies a group of cellular systems.

Guard Time - A time allocated on each mobile transmit slot for transmission so transit time of the signal does not cause collisions between mobiles transmitting on the same frequency.

Half Duplex - The transferring of voice/data in both directions but not at the same time.

Half Rate - The process where only one slot per six slot frames is used to convey all speech or data within a 40 msec interval.

Handoff - A process where a mobile operating on a particular channel will be reassigned to a new channel. This is necessary for two reasons. First, if the mobile moves out of range of one cell site and is within range of another cell site and second, if the mobile has requested a cellular channel with different capabilities. This could mean assignment from a digital channel to an analog channel or assignment from an analog channel to a digital channel.

Home Mobile Station - A mobile that is operating in a cellular system where it has subscribed for service.

Hot Spots - Regions in a cellular service area, which due to traffic patterns, receive an excessive amount of usage.

Improved Mobile Telephone Service (IMTS) - Available in 1964 as the MJ 150 MHz system, it was the first system to offer automatic dialing. With the exception to cellular handoffs, this system is most identical to the cellular system in use today.

In Band Signaling - Signaling that occurs within the 300-3000 Hz audio bandwidth.

Inter-Exchange Carrier - A long distance service provider (i.e. MCI) that provides inter-exchange services between Local Exchange Carriers (LEC).

Intercept - A message sent to the mobile to inform the user of an error or that no service could be established when attempting to place a call.

Interleaving - 1. A process used where data is not sent in direct time sequence to minimize the effect of burst errors. 2. A process of offsetting channel frequencies to increase the reuse capacity of a system.

Intersymbol Interference (ISI) - The result of multipath propagation which results in a distorted received signal. This is due to symbol representation overlaps decision points.

Local Control - A function of the mobile which has been designated to provide special features in addition to those specified by the cellular standard.

Local Exchange Carrier (LEC) - A telephone service provider which furnishes local telephone service to end users.

Loss of Radio Link Continuity {Task} - This task is executed when the mobile cannot confirm a radio link exists between the base and mobile. It results in re-initializing the call when the radio link cannot be maintained. (See Section Call Processing)

Malfunction Timer - A timer which runs separate from all other functions. It continuously counts down and needs to be reset. If the mobile is operating correctly (without failure) this timer will be reset continuously and will not expire. This timer is used to turn off the mobile in case of mobile failure.

Metropolitan Service Area (MSA) - An area designated by the FCC for service to be provided for by a cellular carrier. There are two service providers for each MSA.

Mobile Assisted Handoff (MAHO) - A process where the base requests signal quality information from the mobile which can be used to determine which cell site channel is best suited for handoff. The mobile can provide RSSI information on up to 12 forward channels and BER on its current operating channel. (See Section RF Channel)

Mobile Identification Number (MIN (1,2)) - This is the mobile's telephone number. It is divided into MIN1 and MIN2. MIN1 is the 7 digit portion of the number. MIN2 is the 3 digit area code portion of the number.

Mobile Station (MS) - A receiver transmitter operating in a cellular system. This includes handheld units along with transceiver units installed in vehicles.

Mobile Station Class (MSC) - This is a classification of the power level capability of the mobile. Mobiles may have a high, mid-range, or low power station. The mobile identifies to the base its power level capability by using the Station Class Mark field.

Mobile Station Control Message - A message sent from the base station to the mobile over the analog voice channel which allows assignment to a digital traffic channel. This message was modified in IS-54 to contain two words. Two words are necessary to include all the parameters necessary for assignment to the digital channel.

Mobile Switching Center (MSC) - Similar to the Mobile Telephone Switching Office except it does not have data base support.

Mobile Telephone Switching Office (MTSO) - Includes switching equipment needed to interconnect mobile equipment with the land telephone network and associated data support equipment.

Multipath Propagation - Occurs when the same signal transmitted reaches a point via different paths. This is due to signal reflection and refraction (see RF channel).

Multiplexing - The process of combining several resources over a shared medium. This may be in the form of time sharing (Time Division Multiplexing) where one radio channel is divided into time periods and one resource uses the channel for only the dedicated time allowed.

Narrowband Advanced Mobile Phone Service - A cellular system which narrows the channel bandwidth from 30 kHz to 10 kHz to increase system capacity. It utilizes a majority of the AMPS operation with minor signaling changes.

Non-Wireline Carriers - Cellular service providers that are not engaged in the business of providing landline telephone service.

Number Assignment Module (NAM) - A 32 byte memory storage area which contains user profile data such as MIN (Mobile Identification Number), ESN (Electronic Serial Number), and the registered SID (System Identification).

Operations, Administration and Maintenance (OA&M) - Supervision of the cellular system and its component parts.

Out of Band Signaling - Signaling which occurs outside of the 300-3000 Hz audio bandwidth.

Orders - Messages sent between the mobile and base station.

Overload Class (OLC) [Field] - A field within the global system messages sent to the mobile which indicates if the mobile is authorized to attempt access.

Overload Control - A process used by the system to control the access attempts initiated by mobiles. Overload Class (OLC) bits sent in the overhead message inhibit operation of groups of mobiles.

Overhead Messages - System messages that are sent from the base station to the mobile giving the mobile the necessary parameters to operate in that system.

Paging - The process where the base station sends a message over the control channel informing the mobile a call is incoming.

Paging Channel - A control channel which addresses mobiles directly to alert them of an incoming signal.

Phase Locked Loop (PLL) - A circuit which synchronizes an adjustable oscillator with another more stable oscillator by the comparison of phase between the two signals.[1]

Photogrammetry - A process through which terrain elevation data can be accumulated from using a stereo image or photographs in 3-D.

Pop - The population of a cellular service area for a service provider. This is used for evaluating the worth of a system. The number of pops is multiplied by the price to be paid per pop.

Power Level (PL) - The mobile station's power level. This is the power level relative to the maximum allowable power for that class.

Preorigination Dialing - A process where the dialing sequence takes place prior to the mobile's first communication with the cellular system.

Private Branch Exchange (PBX) - A private switching facility that is used to permit internal call routing and connection to the PSTN.

Protocol Capability Indicator (PCI) [Field] - A bit in the system overhead information which indicates the cell site has digital channel capability.

Protocol Discriminator [Field] - A 2 bit field used on the digital traffic channel. It is reserved for future use for indication of different protocols and the bits must be set to "00."

Rayleigh Fading - The function where the received signal strength will vary due to multipath propagation. A fade usually occurs every wavelength (approximately 16 cm.).

Re-Use Factor - A number which depicts the ability to reuse frequencies at other cell sites. As the reuse factor goes up, the required distance between cells with reuse frequencies increases.

Read Control Filler (RCF) [Field] - A field in the system overhead information data stream that indicates if the mobile must read the control filler messages prior to attempting access to the system.

Reflection - A function where a radiated signal that is incident on a reflective surface will have some or all of its energy reflected from that surface. This is a significant problem with mountains and high rise buildings.

---

1 The oscillator may be replaced by a sinusoidal signal that may have been created in a variety of ways including by a demodulation circuit.

Refraction - A function where a radiated signal on entering a medium of differing propagation characteristics is bent. This is seen at lower frequencies where the ionosphere bends the signals back toward the Earth resulting in signal skipping. This has allowed world radio coverage.

Registration - The process whereby a mobile station identifies itself by sending a message that it is operating in the service area.

Registration Identification - A process where the mobile accesses the cellular network to inform the system it is in its operating area.

Release Request - An order where the base station or the mobile requests a termination of conversation mode.

Reverse Analog Control Channel (RECC) - The FSK modulated channel that completes the control channel signaling transmission path from the Mobile Station to the Base Station.

Reverse Analog Voice Channel (RVC) - The FM channel that completes the voice/traffic channel from the Mobile Station to the Base Station.

Roamer - A mobile station that is operating in a cellular system other than its subscribed system.

Roaming - The process where a mobile is operating in a system other than its registered home system.

Rural Service Area (RSA) - An area designated by the FCC for service to be provided for by cellular carriers. Due to statistical analysis, the demand for cellular in these areas should be less than Metropolitan Service Areas.

SAT Color Code (SCC) [Field] - Additional bits that are sent in the overhead forward control channel message stream to expand the number of available SAT codes from 4 (2 bits) to 64 (6 bits).

Scan of Channels - A process where the mobile unit tunes to a defined set of frequencies and locks on to the strongest signals.

Scan Primary Set of Dedicated Control Channels {Task} - This is the first task the mobile uses to find which signal is the strongest of the dedicated control channels.

Secondary Dedicated Control Channels - A second set of nationwide allocated control channels that may be used by a digital cell site switch.

Sectoring - A process of dividing cell sites where the radiation pattern is divided into sectors by using directional antennas.

Seizure Precursor - A defined bit stream transmitted by the Mobile Station on the reverse analog channel used to synchronize the Base Station receiver.

Serial Number - A 32 bit electronic serial number permanently installed in the mobile. For dual mode mobiles, this number is encrypted by an algorithm "AUTH1" for transmission for Dual Mode capable mobiles.

Serial Number Response Message - This is a message that was added in addition to the requirements of EIA-553 which allows the base station to query the Mobile Station for its unencrypted serial number.

Service Provider - An organization that provides cellular service.

Shortened Burst - A shortened transmit burst used by the mobile when initial transmit occurs in a large diameter cell where timing information has not been established. This is required to overcome propagation delays which may cause burst collisions (overlapping received bursts).

Signaling Tone - A 10 kHz tone mixed in with the analog voice signal which is used as a status change signaling device between the Mobile Station and the Base Station.

Signaling System #7 (SS7) - A Network signaling protocol which uses seven protocol layers that increases the data throughput when compared to the existing X.25 packetized network. It includes physical, data link, network, transport, session, presentation, and application layers.

Slot - See Time Slot.

Slow Associated Control Channel (SACCH) - Out of Band signaling that occurs on the digital traffic channel where messages are transferred by a dedicated number of bits (12) assigned within each time slot.

Soft Capacity Limit - A system subscriber serving capacity limit which allows more users to receive service at a less than optimal quality.

Special Mobile Group (GSM) - Created by CEPT to establish a digital cellular standard to be used in Europe. This system, while theoretically similar to IS-54, will not be compatible with the U.S. system.

Speech Frame - For a full rate traffic channel, this will be a 20 msec period that the speech is sampled. When half rate traffic channel is supported, the sample period will be increased to 40 msec.

Standard Offset Reference (SOR) - This is a time period allocated between the transmit and receive burst that allows antenna diversity measurement. Its period is 44 symbols (approximately 1.8 msec).

Supervisory Audio Tone (SAT) - One of several continuous tones that is mixed in with the modulating audio signal to identify channel interferers of the same RF frequency.

Supplementary Digital Color Code (SDCC(1,2)) [Field] - The additional fields in the forward control channel that operate as Digital Color Codes.

Symbol - Defined for a relative phase shift of the transmitted signal over a specified period of time.

Synthesizer - A frequency generator that can provide any one of the stable RF carrier frequencies required upon direction from the microprocessor in the logic section.

System Identification (SID) [Field] - The field in the forward control channel which holds the system identification number.

Task - A set of steps or processes a transceiver must take to accomplish a function.

Teleservices - Telecommunications services that provide facilities for the transporting and processing of user information.

Thermal Noise - A theoretical power level of noise due to temperature. kTB, where k is boltzmans constant, T is degrees kelvin, B is bandwidth in Hertz.

Time Division Multiple Access (TDMA) - A process of sharing a cellular channel by sharing time between users. Each user is assigned a specific time position.

Time Slot - A particular time period assigned in the digital channel. There are 6 time slots allocated per frame on the digital traffic channel.

Total Access Communications System (TACS) - The cellular system in use in England today. It is an enhanced version of AMPS.

Traffic Channel - The combination of voice and data signals existing in a communication channel.

Trunking - Allows a mobile to be connected to any unused channel in a group of channels for an incoming or outgoing call.

Unequal Cell Loading - A process where cell sites in a general area share or provide a different amount of voice channels. This can be dynamic where channels are redefined on command by MTSO or by the established frequency plan.

User Channel (UCH) - The raw data portion of a channel that is available to the user.

Um Interface - The RF channel between the Base Station and the Cellular Subscriber Station.

Update Overhead Information {Task} - A procedure where the mobile tunes to the strongest dedicated control channel and gathers system overhead information. It uses the information gathered here to determine the paging channels, system ID, and other system parameters.

Update Protocol Capability Indicator {Task} - This is the same task as Update Overhead Information except it has an additional function of determining if the cell site is digital capable.

Verify Overhead Information {Task} - This task requires the mobile to verify the System ID, Roam Status, and Local Control status.

Voltage Controlled Oscillator (VCO) - An oscillator circuit which has an output frequency that changes proportionally with an input voltage.

Voice Mobile Attenuation Code (VMAC) [Field] - A field in the extended address word which commands the mobile to initial power level when assigned to a voice or traffic channel.

Wait For Overhead Message (WFOM) [Field] - A flag in the overhead message which informs the mobile if it must wait for the overhead message before accessing the system.

Waiting for Answer {Task} - A process where the mobile station is waiting for a response from the base station.

Waiting for Order {Task} - A process where the mobile station is waiting for an order from the base station.

Wavelength - The distance covered for one complete cycle of a propagated signal. This can be calculated by dividing the propagation velocity c(speed of light - 300 E6 meters/second) by the number of cycles in one second. For example, the wavelength at 840 MHz is .357 meters (14 inches).

Wireline Carriers - Cellular service providers that are also engaged in the business of landline telephone service. Band B is allocated for these service providers. Some wireline carriers have been authorized to provide service in band A.

Word Error Rate (WER) - The ratio of words received in error with respect to the total number of words sent.

X.25 - A packetized signaling network.

Appendix II - Acronyms

A/D - Analog to Digital

ACK - Acknowledge

ACCOLC - Access Overload Class

AMPS - Advanced Mobile Phone Service

ARTS - Advanced Radio Technology Subcommittee

B/I - Busy Idle Bit

BER - Bit Error Rate

BIS - Busy Idle Status

BS - Base Station

C/N - Carrier to Noise Ratio

C/I - Carrier to Interference Ratio

CAF - Cellular Anti-Fraud

CCIR - International Radio Consultative Committee

CCITT - International Telegraph and Telephone Consultative Committee

CCLIST - Control Channel List

CDMA - Code Division Multiple Access

CDVCC - Coded Digital Voice Color Code

CEC - Commission of the European Communities

CEPT - European Conference of Posts and Telecommunications

CELP - Code Excited Linear Predictive

CMAC - Control Mobile Attenuation Code

CoDec - Coder/Decoder

CPA - Combined Paging and Access

CQM - Channel Quality Measurement

CSMA - Carrier Sense Multiple Access

CSS - Cellular Subscriber Station

CTIA - Cellular Telecommunications Industry Association

CT2 - Cordless Technology 2nd Generation

CP - Cellular Provider

CPE - Cellular Provider Equipment

DCC - Digital Color Code

DECT - Digital European Cordless Telephone

DQPSK - Differential Quadrature Phase Shift Keying

DSI - Digital Speech Interpolation

DTC - Digital Traffic Channel

DTMF - Dual Tone Multiple Frequency

DTX - Discontinuous Transmission

DVCC - Digital Voice Color Code

E^{2}PROM - Electrically Eraseable Programmable Read Only Memory

EIA - Electronics Industries Association

EMI - Electromagnetic Interference

EP - Extended Protocol Indicator

EPROM - Eraseable Programmable Read Only Memory

ERP - Effective Radiated Power

ESN - Electronic Serial Number

ETACS - Enhanced Totally Accessed Communications System

ETDMA - Extended Time Division Multiple Access

FACCH - Fast Associated Control Channel

FCC - Federal Communications Commission

FDM - Frequency Division Multiplexing

FDMA - Frequency Division Multiple Access

FDTC - Forward Digital Traffic Channel

FEC - Forward Error Correction

FIRSTCHA - First Access Channel

FIRSTCHP - First Paging Channel

FOCC - Forward (Analog) Control Channel

FPLMTS - Future Public Land Mobile Telephone System

FSK - Frequency Shift Keying

FVC - Forward Analog Voice Channel

GSA - Geographical Service Area

GSM - Special Mobile Group

IEC - Inter Exchange Carrier

IMTS - Improved Mobile Telephone Service

IPR - Intellectual Property Rights

ISDN - Integrated Services Digital Network

IVCD - Initial Voice Channel Designation

LASTCHA - Last Access Channel

LASTCHP - Last Paging Channel

LEC - Local Exchange Carrier

LSB - Least Significant Bit

MAHO - Mobile Assisted Hand Off

MIN - Mobile Identification Number

MIPS - Million Instructions Per Second

MS - Mobile Station

MSA - Metropolitan Statistical Area

MSB - Most Significant Bit

MSC - Mobile Switching Center

MTSO - Mobile Telephone Switching Office

NAM - Number Assignment Module

NAMPS - Narrowband Advanced Mobile Phone Service

NAWC - Number of Additional Words Coming

OA&M - Operations, Administration and Maintenance

OLC - Overload Class

ORDQ - Order Qualifier

OSI - Open System Interconnection

PBX - Private Branch Exchange

PCI - Protocol Capability Indicator

PCM - Pulse Coded Modulation

PCN - Personal Communications Network

PIN - Personal Identification Number

PLL - Phase Locked Loop

PLMN - Public Land Mobile Network

POTS - Plain Old Telephone Service

PSCC - Present SAT Color Code

PSK - Phase Shift Keying

PSTN - Phone System Terminal Network

PTT - Postal Telephone and Telegraph

PUC - Public Utilities Commission

RAM - Random Access Memory

RCF - Read Control Filler

RDTC - Reverse Digital Traffic Channel

RECC - Reverse (Analog) Control Channel

RELP - Residual Excited Linear Predictive

ROM - Read Only Memory

RSA - Rural Service Area

RSSI - Received Signal Strength Indicator

RTC - Reverse Traffic Channel Digital

RVC - Reverse Analog Voice Channel

SACCH - Slow Associated Control Channel

SBI - Shortened Burst Indicator

SCC - Sat Color Code

SCM - Station Class Mark

SDCC(1,2) - Supplementary Digital Color Codes

SID - System Identification

SOR - Standard Offset Reference

SS7 - Signaling System #7

ST - Signaling Tone

SWR - Standing Wave Ratio

TA - Time Alignment

TACS - Totally Accessed Communications System

TDD - Time Division Duplex

TDM - Time Division Multiplexing

TDMA - Time Division Multiple Access

TIA - Telecommunications Industries Association

uCell - Micro Cell

uP - Microprocessor

UCH - User Channel

UPR - User Performance Requirements

VCO - Voltage Controlled Oscillator

VCS - Voice Controlled Switch

VMAC - Voice Mobile Attenuation Code

VSELP - Vector-Sum Excited Linear Predictive Coding

VSWR - Voltage Standing Wave Ratio

WER - Word Error Rate

WFOM - Wait For Overhead Message

Appendix III - Standards

The following standards exist for manufacture of cellular systems. Standards can be obtained by contacting the EIA (Electronic Industries Association) at:

Electronic Industries Association

2001 Eye Street N.W.

Washington, D.C. 20006

U.S.A.

IS-41

This is for Intersystems connection and is applicable for switch manufacturers. It offers new features which allow the passing of information between the home system and a visited system. It consists of five parts:

IS-41.1 - Cellular Radiotelecommunications Intersystems Operations: Functional Overview

IS-41.2 - Cellular Radiotelecommunications Intersystems Operations: Intersystem Handoff

IS-41.3 - Cellular Radiotelecommunications Intersystems Operations: Automatic Roaming

IS-41.4 - Cellular Radiotelecommunications Intersystems Operations: Operations, Administration, and Maintenance

IS-41.5 - Cellular Radiotelecommunications Intersystems Operations: Data Communications

IS-3D

This is the standard for Analog Cellular functional operability.

EIA-553

This standard has replaced IS-3-D.

IS-19-B Recommended Minimum Standards for 800 MHz Cellular Subscriber Units

This provides specific definitions, measurement techniques, and minimum performance specifications for cellular terminal equipment. It is to be used in conjunction with EIA-553.

IS-20-A Recommended Minimum Standards for 800 MHz Cellular Land Station equipment.

IS-53 Intersystem Features

IS-54 Digital Cellular

IS-55 Minimum

IS-56 Minimum

Standards for the manufacture of TACS cellular systems can be obtained by contacting:

Racal-Vodafone Limited

The Courtyard

2-4 London Road

Newbury

Berkshire, RG13 1JL

England

+44 (0)635-33251

Fax +44 (0)635-31127

TACS/ETACS

Standards for the manufacture of GSM cellular systems can be obtained by contacting:

Mm. S. Poli

ETSI/GSM-PT12

9, rue Georges Pitard (23" etage)

F, 75015 Paris

Fax +33-1-45-31-16-87

Standards for the manufacture of NMT-450/NMT-900 cellular systems can be obtained by contacting:

Hans Myhre

Chairman of NMT Norwegian Telecom

Oslo, Norway

+47-2-488-990

Fax +47-2-488-720

Standards for the manufacture of RC2000 cellular systems can be obtained by contacting:

France Telecom

6 place d'Alleray

75740 Paris Cedex 15

+33-1-44-44-22-22

Appendix IV
World Cellular Systems

Country	AMPS	TACS	NMT-450	NMT-900	CT2	GSM[9]	Other
Algeria				X			
Andorra			X				
Argentina	X						
Australia	X						
Austria		X	X				
Antigua & Barbuda	X						
Bahamas	X						
Bahrain		X					
Barbados	X						
Belgium			X^3				
Bermuda	X						
Bolivia	X						
Brazil	X						
British Virgin Islands	X						
Brunei	X						
Bulgaria							
Canada	X						
Cayman Islands	X						
Chile	X						
China		X^7	X^{10}				
Colombia	X						
Costa Rica	X						
Curacao	X						
Cyprus				X^2			
Czechoslovakia	X						
Denmark			X^1	X^2			
Dominican Republic	X						
Egypt	X	X					X
Estonia			X				
Faroe Islands			X				
Finland			X^1	X^2			
France				X^{11}	X		RC 2000
Gabon	X						
Germany						X	C-450
Grenada	X						
Greece						X	

Country	AMPS	TACS	NMT-450	NMT-900	CT2	GSM[9]	Other
Guadeloupe	X						
Guatemala	X						
Hong Kong	X	X	X				
Hungary		X	X				
Iceland			X^1				
India		X					
Indonesia	X	X	X^5				
Ireland		X					
Israel	X						
Italy		X^6				X	RMTS
Jamaica	X						
Japan							JTACS
							NTACS
							NAMTS
Jordan	X						
Kenya	X						
Kuwait		X					
Luxembourg			X^3				
Macao		X					
Malaysia	X	X	X				
Malta		X					
Mauritius		X					
Mexico	X						
Morocco		X	X				
Netherlands			X^3	X^2		X	
Netherlands Antilles	X						
New Zealand	X						
Nigeria		X					
Norway			X^1	X^2			
Oman			X				
Pakistan		X					
Panama	X						
Peru	X						
Philippines	X						
Poland							
Portugal							C-450
Puerto Rico	X						
Saudi Arabia			X^4				
Singapore	X	X	X				
Samoa (American)	X						
South Africa							Netz-C
South Korea	X						

Country	AMPS	TACS	NMT-450	NMT-900	CT2	GSM[9]	Other
Spain		X	X			X	
Sri Lanka		X					
St. Kitts	X						
St. Lucia	X						
St. Maarten	X						
St. Vincent & Grenadines	X						
Sweden			X[1]	X[2]			Comvik+
Switzerland				X[2]			
Taiwan	X						
Thailand	X	X	X[5]	X			
Tunisia			X				
Turkey				X[12]			
U. A. E.		X					
U. S. A.	X						IS-54
(Guam)	X						
United Kingdom		X[6]			X	X[8]	
Uruguay	X						
U. S. S. R.							
(Leningrad)			X				
(Moscow)			X				
Venezuela	X						
Virgin Islands	X						
Yugoslavia							
Zaire	X						

NOTE:
1, 2, 5, 6. These NMT mobile units are compatible with each other.
3. These mobile units are compatible with each other and use the ATF version of NMT.
4. Saudi Arabia has two bands, each are NMT-450.
7. China has two bands for TACS, 450 MHz, and 900 MHz.
8. The GSM standard will be used for two systems. One standard and one at a frequency of 1.8 GHz (DCS-1800).
9. Service to begin early 1990s.
10. NMT 450 system in oil fields.
11. The SFR network operates @ 450 MHz but applies the NMT-900 standard.
12. Operates at 410 MHz.

Source:
1. U.S. Department of Commerce
2. Fintech (U.K. Financial Times)
3. Cellular Business, February 1991
4. Nokia Corporation, Finland, March 1991
5. Marconi Corporation, United Kingdom, March 1991
6. Antenna Specialists, U.S.A., March 1991
7. Ericsson Corporation, Press Release, December, 1990

A

Access 1-6, **1-8, 1-10**
    System 1-8, 4-11, **5-23, 5-25**

    Channel 2-12, **2-16,** 4-2, **5-13, 5-22, 5-23, 5-26, 5-44, 6-17**

Adaptive equalization **5-38**

Advanced mobile phone service (AMPS) **2-31, 2-32, 7-9, 8-2, 8-3, 8-12**

AmplitudeModulation 2-3, 2-4

Analog
    Mobile Station 2-1, **2-18, 2-33, 4-13, 5-13, 5-45**

    Base Station 3-1, 3-6, **4-16, 4-20, 6-23**

Antennas
    beamwidth **2-31**

    directional 1-3, **3-12, 3-36, 3-38,** 4-20

    mismatch **2-29, 2-30**

    omnidirectional 1-16, **3-11, 3-12,** 4-20

Authentication
    Center (AC) **3-17, 3-18**

    procedure 4-11, **4-12, 4-23, 5-22, 5-26, 5-45, 6-7, 6-8, 6-23, 7-5, 7-10**

Automatic Gain Control (AGC) **2-25, 2-26**

B

Bandwidth 2-21, **2-24, 2-25, 2-27, 3-20, 3-22,** 4-5, **4-6, 4-7, 4-19,** 5-1, **5-10, 5-31, 5-33, 5-37, 5-40, 5-44, 8-1, 8-2, 8-4, 8-5, 8-6, 8-7, 8-8, 8-9**

Base Station (BS) 1-4, **1-5, 1-6, 1-8, 1-10, 1-11, 1-14** through **1-20,** 2-3, **2-5, 2-7, 2-8, 2-9, 2-14, 2-16, 2-23, 2-24,** 3-1 through **3-8, 3-15, 3-23** through **3-26, 3-28,** 4-4, **4-7, 4-11** through **4-14, 4-16** through **4-20, 4-22, 4-23, 5-10, 5-13, 5-14, 5-36,** 6-1 through **6-5, 6-8, 6-10, 6-13, 6-20, 6-21, 6-23, 7-2, 7-5, 7-9, 7-10, 8-9** through **8-11**

Baseband 2-3, **2-26, 3-11, 6-5, 6-6**

Bit error rate (BER) **5-33, 5-37, 6-13, 6-16**

Blank and burst 1-8, **2-8, 2-9, 2-16, 2-32, 4-11, 5-14**